Organisms and Evolution

4/e

John Dickerman

Mc Graw Hill Education

ISBN-13: 978-1-264-11433-7
ISBN-10: 1-264-11433-8

Solutions Program Manager: Steve Tomecek
Project Manager: Lisa Haverland
Cover Photo Credits: 85758317.tif © Science Photo Library RF/Getty Images

ACKNOWLEDGMENTS

Preparing a book of this kind is a humbling experience - it quickly reveals how little one knows. There is no doubt that the topics included in this book range far beyond the areas I can claim any kind of expertise in. Luckily, while on the faculty at Northern Illinois University, I have been able to work with many talented scientists who have the expertise I lack. I owe a special debt to Professor Arthur Weis (currently at the University of California) who taught me a great deal both about biology and how to teach it. His influence can be found throughout this book, but especially in the first three chapters, which are based on exercises he taught me years ago. Professor Ronald Toth was another important mentor. He suggested many appropriate topics for the chapters on plant diversity and provided me with a concise evolutionary framework with which to organize them. Patrick McCarthy was indispensable when I had questions about microbiology. In a more general way, I benefited from many helpful discussions with Drs. Richard Becker, Bethia King, Peter Meserve, and Paul Sorenson. Dr. Daniel Olson gave me much practical help in the preparation of this book, along with valuable insights from his own experiences.

PREFACE
TO THE STUDENT

Modern biology is an almost impossibly large field. In a single department, sometimes in a single laboratory, may work chemists, molecular biologists, physiologists, naturalists, and many others, all of whom will have difficulty understanding each other when they talk about their work. Yet you, a beginning student, will be expected to survey this huge science and come out with a basic understanding of all of these different areas.

It is my hope that this book will help you with this daunting task. The standard I have tried to follow in selecting and presenting different topics is not what is easy or convenient to do in the teaching laboratory, but rather what best illustrates the important principles of biology. You should therefore be able to experience firsthand what you read about in your text or hear in lecture. These experiences should help you to understand the principles better and will also give you mental pictures to aid your memory as you go into exams. You will also start the process of becoming scientists, who, ideally, should take nothing on faith or by authority, but should instead demand a clear demonstration of any assertion.

As a result of this approach, you will find the exercises in this book to be a varied lot indeed. Some will be simple and foolproof, while others will be complex and challenging. Some phenomena will come out in dramatic, even colorful, displays; others will only reveal themselves after numerous measurements and sophisticated calculations. Although written for the beginning student, these experiments are intended to mirror the practice of biology in modern research laboratories. As you work through them you should get a better idea of which areas of biology you are suited for and which areas interest you least.

Study Hints

Because of the diversity of these topics, you will be evaluated in different ways at different times. You will often be quizzed over recently completed chapters. To help you prepare for such quizzes, a list of important terms is collected at the end of each chapter. You would be well-advised to write out the definitions of these terms and learn them. Also work at becoming comfortable with the scientific names of organisms (italicized throughout). Take the time to learn the formal names and fundamental characteristics of each group (kingdom, phylum). This will at times seem like tedious memorization, but the fact is, there is no biology without organisms. Learning the general principles without being able to refer to real examples has no practical value.

CONTENTS

CHAPTER 1
DEMONSTRATING SELECTION

INTRODUCTION

The experiment described in this chapter deals with evolution. It will be easier to interpret after we have completed chapters 2 and 3, but since this experiment takes several weeks to perform, we will begin with it now.

In popular usage, **evolution** has become a somewhat misunderstood term. In its simplest aspect, evolution refers to the observable changes in the average genotype of a population over time. It is important to remember that the basic unit of evolution is the population, not the individual – although an individual may change during its life, such changes do not become incorporated in subsequent generations. By *individual* we do not necessarily mean an individual organism – we could also study individual genes in a population of genes, or individual cells within an organism. For example, a genome could be said to evolve when the genes within it duplicate, change, or are lost. A classic example of an evolving population of cells is provided by the immune system, where the presence of a disease tends to select for antibody-producing cells that can fight the disease. Nevertheless, in each case it is the population of organisms, genes, or cells that is evolving as the distribution of its members changes.

Only those traits which are genetically determined can be passed on to an individual's offspring. In the following experiment you will set up a population of fruit flies of known genetic composition. You will study the population for several generations and observe any changes which occur in the frequencies of the test alleles in the population as a whole.

DROSOPHILA MELANOGASTER

The modern study of genetics began a century ago with the work of T.H. Morgan. Morgan experimented with the common fruit fly, **Drosophila melanogaster**, which has since become a standard organism for genetics studies. Fruit flies have several characteristics which make them useful for such work, the most important being that they can be raised in great numbers in relatively small spaces and that they can complete a new generation in 2-3 weeks. Since the time of Morgan numerous traits have been examined in *Drosophila*, and many genes have been traced to specific locations on one of the fruit fly's four pairs of chromosomes.

Specific traits in *Drosophila* are always referenced with respect to "normal" or **wild** type flies. Wild flies have red eyes, are free of malformed wings and appendages, and thrive under standard culture conditions. **Mutant** flies differ from wild in some structural or physiological trait. The nomenclature of fruit fly genetics has been adapted slightly so that it expresses not only whether a trait is dominant or recessive, but also whether it is a wild or mutant allele. All wild alleles, whether dominant or recessive, are designated +. Mutant alleles are given a one- or two-letter abbreviation which is capitalized in the case of dominant alleles. For example, the recessive allele e, when homozygous, gives the fly body a dark ebony color. Ebony flies are genotype e/e, wild are +/+, and normal-looking heterozygotes are +/e. Similarly, plum-colored eyes are caused by the dominant allele *Pm*. Wild type flies have the genotype +/+, and the plum phenotype can be caused by both the *Pm/Pm* and *Pm/+* genotypes.

THE HARDY-WEINBERG EQUATION

The fact that one allele is dominant over another allele does not mean that that allele is more common than the recessive allele or even that it will become more common over time – dominance refers only to which phenotype will be expressed in a heterozygote. Dominance and recessiveness have no direct bearing on allele frequencies.

At the beginning of this century, two geneticists, working independently, pointed out that in an ideal population allele frequencies would settle into an equilibrium in the absence of outside forces. By "outside forces" we mean some factor that would force the population to change genetically – natural selection, mutation, or an influx of new genes by immigration. An "ideal population" is large and its members mate randomly (i.e., there is no sexual selection). This idea is called the **Hardy-Weinberg Theorem** after the two scientists.

For a population at Hardy-Weinberg equilibrium, there is an algebraic relationship between genotypes and gene frequencies. For example, assume that for some trait there are only two alleles, a dominant and recessive. In the entire population a fraction, **p**, of the genes are the dominant allele and the rest, **q**, are recessive. Obviously, the two fractions must add up to 100%:

$$p+q = 1$$

If mating is truly random, then any allele is free to pair up with any other allele, and the odds of doing so are based solely on the frequencies of the alleles. The frequency of a combination is found by multiplying the frequencies of the parts. (For example, the chance of getting a "heads" on a coin toss is 50% or 0.5. The chance of getting two heads if you toss two coins together is 0.5 X 0.5 = 0.25, 25%.) Therefore we need to square both sides of the equation:

$$(p+q)(p+q) = 1^2$$

or

$$p^2 + 2pq + q^2 = 1$$

where p^2 = the fraction of dominant homozygotes, $2pq$ = the fraction of heterozygotes, and q^2 = the fraction of recessive homozygotes. You can't tell the difference between dominant homozygotes and heterozygotes because they have the same phenotype, but it is easy to measure the frequency of the recessive homozygotes. From there you can figure out the rest. Let's say that 36% of a population shows the recessive phenotype. That means that $q^2 = 0.36$. Therefore q = 0.6. Since p + q = 1, p must equal 0.4. Therefore 16% ($0.16 = 0.4^2$) are dominant homozygotes and 48% ($2pq = 2(0.4)(0.6)=0.48$) are heterozygotes.

Strictly speaking, the Hardy-Weinberg equation works only in ideal cases. However, unless a population is, for some reason, obviously far from equilibrium, the equation will give a reasonable estimate of allele frequencies based on observed phenotypes. In the following experiments the populations will not be in true equilibrium because selection may be taking place. Nevertheless, experience has shown that it is close enough in any given week that the estimates obtained using the Hardy-Weinberg equation are reasonable. This means that we do not need to employ complex breeding procedures to directly measure the allele frequencies.

INVESTIGATIONS WITH NATURAL SELECTION

You will be working with both wild type and mutant flies in this experiment. The mutant alleles will be for recessive somatic traits. Your lab instructor will describe these traits to you and demonstrate how to tell the difference between the wild and mutant flies. You will also be shown how to anesthetize the flies and how to manipulate them with a soft brush or aspirator, and how to tell the difference between a male and a female fly.

NOTE REGARDING ANESTHETIC: The chemical you will be using to anesthetize the flies (either commercial *FlyNap* or a solution of triethylamine) should be used with reasonable caution. Do not expose yourself to the fumes any longer than necessary. These fumes can be irritating to the nose and eyes.

Preparation of the population cages

1.   The class will be divided into six groups. Each group will maintain a plastic cage with a population of wild and mutant flies. The top of each cage is removable and has two 1 inch holes in it. The bottom of each cage has two 1.5 inch holes. Plug the small holes in the top with small foam plugs. Place a foam ring in one of the large holes in the bottom of the cage.

2.   Place 7.5 ml (1/2 tablespoon) of fly food into a glass vial and add 10 ml water. In a few minutes the food should absorb the water and form a moist blue gel about 3 cm high. Insert the vial into the foam ring. The vial should fit snugly with no gaps through which flies might escape.

3.   Plug the other large hole with a large plug for now; in a few weeks you will add a second vial of fresh food in this opening. The cage should resemble figure 1.1.

Figure 1.1.   Fly cage set up

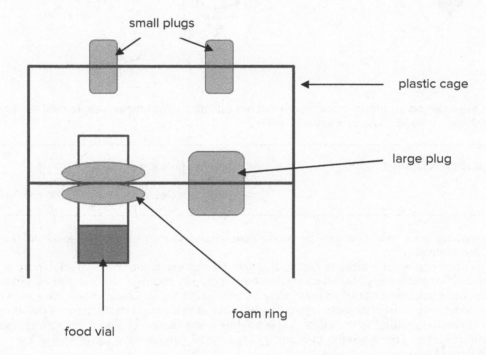

4.   After the cage is prepared, obtain some anesthetized flies from the stocks. Exactly which flies your group will use depends on which of the following experiments you have been assigned to do. Separate 20 <u>females</u> (cf. figure 1.2) from the stocks – no males will be added to the cultures, but it is safe to assume that most of the females are pregnant and ready to lay eggs.

5.   Place the flies in the plastic portion of the cage. Do not put them directly into the food vial where they might suffocate in the soft food.

Figure 1.2. Comparison of male (left) and female fruit flies

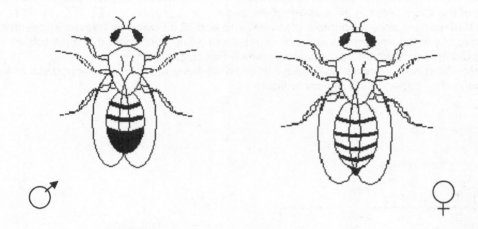

6.   Put the top of the cage on and tape it down so it will not fall off. It is not necessary to seal the top completely with tape unless obvious gaps are visible.

Be sure the cage is labeled with:	what type of flies are present your section the initials of at least one member of your group

Place the cage where your instructor directs, taking care when you move it that the food vial does not fall out of the foam ring.

7.   In your lab notebook construct a table to record the data for this experiment. There should be a column for the date of each entry, the number of wild phenotypes counted, the number of mutant phenotypes counted, and the calculated frequency of the mutant allele. There should be space in the table for at least nine entries (today's being the first). In the first entry simply record how many mutant and wild flies you added to the cage. Because these flies were all taken from pure stocks, they are all homozygotes. <u>Therefore the frequency of the mutant allele is the same as the percentage of mutant flies</u>.

8.   In one week, after the flies have had time to lay their eggs, remove the adult flies.

9.   When the second generation adults emerge in about 2 weeks, you will count the new numbers of each phenotype. Since no males were added to the cage when you set it up, the second generation will still be all homozygotes (the inseminations all occurred in pure culture). <u>Therefore the frequency of the mutant allele will still be the same as the percentage of mutant flies</u>.

10. After you count the second-generation flies, remove the large plug from the bottom of the cage and replace it with a foam ring. Add a second food vial to the cage.

11. Continue the experiment through several generations. Count the phenotypes every week and <u>replace</u> the counted flies. Allow the population to grow and let competition drive selection. Change the food vials as they dry up.

12.   After the second generation you will need to calculate allele frequencies. Estimate the allele frequencies using the Hardy-Weinberg equation, based upon the observed frequency of the recessive phenotype. Since this will be an evolving population, the Hardy-Weinberg relationship will not actually hold true for this situation, and you may occasionally see evidence that your calculated estimates are off (for example, one week you may see no recessive phenotypes and conclude that the allele has disappeared, only to see it reappear in the next generation). However, the estimates will be close enough to show the general trends over several generations.

Each group will set up a cage with <u>one</u> of the following populations:

Controls
These cages will start out with 20 females of a single type - either completely wild or completely mutant. There will be no evolution in these cages. They serve to show how the population of each type of fly will grow in the absence of competition. There will be three controls: wild, mutant 1, and mutant 2.

Single mutant competition
These cages start with a population of 10 wild females and 10 mutant females. Therefore the initial allele frequency of the mutant will be 50%. You will see if it changes due to competition with the wild flies. There will only be one mutant allele per cage, so there will be two of these cages, one for each mutant.

Double mutant competition
This cage will be started with 10 wild females and 10 females exhibiting <u>both</u> mutant traits. At the start each mutant allele frequency will be 50%. At first, the mutants will either exhibit both mutations or none at all, but as the population evolves, you may find flies showing just a single mutation. Therefore <u>you will need to count how many flies have each mutation, how many have both, and how many have neither</u>. Check to be sure your subtotals equal the total number of flies for each count. This experiment will investigate whether natural selection can promote new genetic combinations in a population.

The data for multiple class sections will be pooled at the end of the experiment so that we will have a sample of thousands of flies. You will see why this is important in chapter 3.

When you are able to examine the pooled data, look for reproducible signs of selection. What would the data be like if the mutant frequency increased in some classes but decreased in others? Do the data indicate that the same trends were observed in most classes? What do the control stocks tell you about each strain of flies? Is one type of fly naturally more fit than another, or does relative fitness depend on the mix of alleles present in the population? Are mutations always harmful?

A NOTE ABOUT RECORD KEEPING: When working with many live organisms, the unexpected often happens. Be sure to record any unplanned or unanticipated events in your notebook, as these may be very important in interpreting your results later. (For example, if some of your mutants <u>accidentally</u> die, it will certainly alter the mutant allele frequency in future generations!)

Important Terms

Drosophila melanogaster
evolution
Hardy-Weinberg equation
mutant
wild type

CHAPTER 2
PHENOTYPIC VARIATION

INTRODUCTION

Late in the 18th century, Thomas Malthus, an English clergyman interested in economics, observed that there was a tremendous potential for population growth in man. This observation came early in the industrial revolution when the population of many small villages in the north of England increased dramatically, turning the villages into major cities in just a few decades. (He was probably also influenced by the writings of Benjamin Franklin, who wrote about even bigger population increases in England's American colonies.) In his *Essay On The Principle Of Population*, Malthus wrote that "nature has scattered the seeds of life abroad with the most profuse and liberal hand [but] has been comparatively sparing in the room and the nourishment necessary to rear them." He concluded that famine, disease, and privation were the inevitable consequences of overpopulation, and ultimately a necessary check on population growth.

Charles Darwin was very impressed by Malthus' essay. As a naturalist, he applied Malthus' ideas to all species, for he knew that a single tree could produce thousands of seeds and a single insect hundreds of eggs. Since only a fraction of these offspring could survive and reproduce successfully, Darwin concluded that the competitive pressures inherent in nature acted to sort out the best adapted individuals from those less suited to a particular environment. If the differences selected for were genetically determined, then the characteristics of the most successful individuals should become more common in the population as a whole over time. The principle that differing levels of fitness determine which types of organisms survive and reproduce is called **natural selection**.

Natural selection was an innovative idea. Others before Darwin had suggested theories of evolution, but these tended to be based on the idea that characteristics acquired during life could be passed on to offspring if they proved useful. Darwin realized that novel characteristics need not be acquired during life because they already exist within the natural variation among the different members of a population. He wrote that

> natural selection is daily and hourly scrutinizing, throughout the world, the slightest variations, rejecting those that are bad, preserving and adding up all that are good; silently and insensibly working . . . at the improvement of each organic being . . .

Biologists have been studying the variation in populations ever since.

QUANTIFYING VARIATION

We all know that not all humans are alike — certainly we have no trouble recognizing friends and relatives we know well. People who deal regularly with other species realize that this same principle holds true for other organisms too. Dog breeders can tell seemingly identical puppies apart, dairy farmers can keep track of individual cows, and grape growers know which vines are heartiest and bear the most fruit. One reason Darwin was able to elucidate the principle of natural selection was that for years as a naturalist he had collected numerous specimens of plants and animals and had developed a good appreciation for their individual differences.

In seeking to find a way to measure the variation within a group of individuals, scientists have adopted a mathematical tool called the **frequency distribution**. A frequency distribution is a representation of the number of individuals in each phenotypic class. An example of how frequency distributions can be used in evolutionary biology is provided by the peppered moth (*Biston betularia*), which exhibits both light- and dark-colored phenotypes. Two centuries ago the lighter moths were the most common, but in areas that have been exposed to industrial pollution and soot the darker variety has become more numerous (birds have a hard time finding and eating the dark moths when they alight on sooty surfaces). Natural selection did not cause the light moths to become dark, rather, it caused the dark coloration to become more frequent over several generations. Thus the evolutionary change is described by shifting frequency distributions of the light and dark phenotypes. All evolutionary changes are essentially shifts in frequency distributions.

DISCONTINUOUS VARIATION

Some phenotypic traits assume one of several alternative states, without any intermediate states being possible. For example, human blood types can be either A, B, AB, or O. Every person has one of these types, and no intermediate phenotypes exist. The traits described by classic Mendelian genetics are examples of such **discontinuous traits**. A frequency distribution for a discontinuous trait can be represented as a table showing the frequency of alternate states of the trait. The following table represents body color in a hypothetical population of fruit flies:

light body	ebony body	total
62	38	100

This table has one dimension – it shows a variation in one trait only. Often individuals will simultaneously differ for a number of traits. A multidimensional table can be used to describe variation in such cases. Assume, for instance, that the flies listed in the table above also varied in their wing shapes. The following is a two dimensional table for the two traits:

	light body	ebony body	wing shape total
vestigial wing	44	28	72
straight wing	18	10	28
body color total	62	38	100

An alternate way of displaying discontinuous data is with a bar graph. Here the various states of the traits are arranged along the x-axis and the number of individuals showing each state is proportional to the height of the corresponding bar. The data from the previous table are graphed this way in figure 2.1.

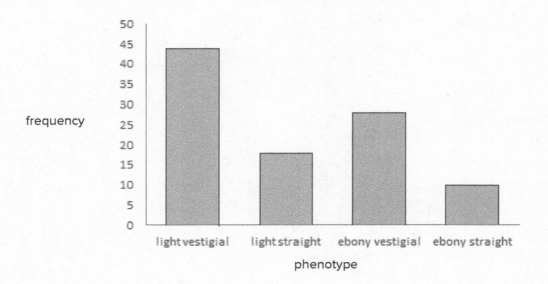

Figure 2.1. Frequency of color-wing phenotypes in *Drosophila* sample.

CONTINUOUS VARIATION

Most of the visible variation among individuals in a population is not due to discontinuous traits but rather to **continuous traits**. These are characters that can be measured on a continuous scale (e.g., height, weight, metabolic rate, etc.). Instead of having two or three possible states, these traits can have an infinite number of values. Consider height in humans. We normally round off measured values to the nearest inch, say for example, 70 inches. But the actual heights of people reporting a height of 70 inches could be anywhere from 69.5 to 70.4999. . . (to any number of decimal places you can measure) inches. One could imagine an infinite number of people in that range, and no two with <u>exactly</u> the same height. Even though continuous traits can have an infinite number of values, for practical purposes real data on such traits are often rounded off to fewer significant figures than the accuracy of each measurement would allow. This allows the data to be handled in workable sets. (In the example above, it is certainly possible to measure height to the nearest fraction of an inch, but rounding to the nearest inch makes the data easier to handle.)

The methods used to describe continuous variation are more complex than those used for discontinuous variation. Frequency tables are very seldom used since one column is required for every potential value of the trait, and even with rounding off there are many potential values.

To illustrate the methods for describing continuous variation, let us again use a hypothetical population of fruit flies. This time assume that body weight was measured, with the following values (in µg) obtained: 54, 57, 55, 55, 53, 54, 56, 51, 52, 52, 54, 55, 53, 54, 56, 53, 54. It is difficult to discern any pattern in variation by simply looking at the raw data. A better presentation of the data is in the form of a special bar graph called a **histogram** (figure 2.2). In a histogram the value of the trait is indicated on the x-axis and the number of times it is observed is indicated on the y-axis. The bars of a histogram are always shown touching along the side in order to remind the viewer that the real values are continuous even though they are rounded off.

Figure 2.2. Frequency of body weights in *Drosophila* sample.

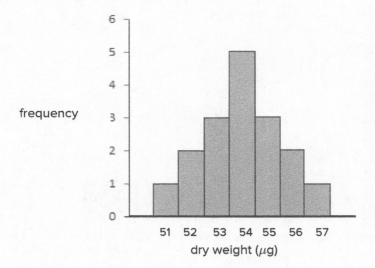

A striking characteristic of this example is the central tendency of the frequency distribution – many individuals are near the middle weight, but there are fewer and fewer individuals as the weights become more extreme. These data resemble a "bell-shaped" or **normal curve**. Many biological traits have a normal distribution.

Evolution is measured as a change in trait distribution, and while histograms are good at illustrating individual distributions, they are clumsy tools for comparing several different distributions. It is therefore useful to have a mathematical index that summarizes the entire distribution. Such indices are provided by the branch of mathematics called **statistics**. Statistics is a large field concerned with many aspects of probability distributions (trait frequency distributions are one kind of probability distribution). We will consider three statistics which together give a very good description of a probability distribution.

The middle of the distribution is described by the **mean**. The mean is simply the arithmetic average of the data:

$$\bar{x} = \sum x / n$$

where $\bar{x}$ is the mean, **x** are the individual data values, and **n** is the number of data values.

The **variance** describes the spread around the mean. A low variance indicates that the individuals are similar to one another while a high variance indicates that they differ more. The formula for the variance is:

$$s^2 = \frac{\sum(x - \bar{x})^2}{(n - 1)}$$

where s^2 is the variance and the other variables are as above. The term $(x - \bar{x})$ is the deviation of any individual value from the mean. Thus the variance represents the average <u>squared</u> deviation for the sample.[*] The average squared deviation is used instead of the average deviation because the average deviation always equals zero – the highs and the lows cancel each other exactly (try it yourself and see). Defined by this formula, the variance has mathematical properties that make it useful in many statistical analyses.

For simple comparisons, the **standard deviation** is adequate to describe differences in the spread of a distribution. The standard deviation is defined as:

$$s = \sqrt{s^2}$$

That is, the standard deviation is the square root of the average squared deviation. Going back and forth between the square and the square root is not as illogical as it seems. Squaring the deviation before taking the average ensures that the average will not automatically be zero, and taking the square root after averaging gives a number in the original units of the measurement. In our example of fruit fly weights, both the average weight and the standard deviation would be in units of μg.

An example of how these statistics are calculated is in the following table. The data from the fruit fly example are tabulated along with each value's deviation from the mean and the squared deviation.

Statistical analysis of *Drosophila* body weight data	Observed weight x (μg)	Deviation from mean $x - \bar{x}$ (μg)	Squared deviation $(x - \bar{x})^2$
	54	0	0
	57	3	9
	55	1	1
	55	1	1
	53	−1	1
	54	0	0
	56	2	4
	51	−3	9
	52	−2	4
	52	−2	4
	54	0	0
	55	1	1
	53	−1	1
	54	0	0
	56	2	4
	53	−1	1
	54	0	0
	$\sum x = 918$		$\sum (x - \bar{x})^2 = 40$

mean: $= \sum x / n = 918/17 =$ **54.0** μg

variance: $s^2 = \sum (x - \bar{x})^2 / (n - 1) = 40/16 =$ **2.5**

standard deviation: $s^2 = \sqrt{s^2} = \sqrt{2.5} =$ **1.6** μg

---

[*] Normally the average would be obtained by dividing by n instead of n-1. However, the variance is derived from another statistic, the mean. We divide by the **degrees of freedom** instead of n as a way of correcting for taking a statistic of a statistic.

INVESTIGATIONS WITH MEASURING VARIATION

Investigation #1   **Measuring discontinuous variation in human fingerprints**
In the fruit fly experiment for chapter 1 you measured the frequency distribution of the wild and mutant alleles of one or two discontinuous traits. For each trait there were only two possible values. In this exercise you will examine your fingerprints for a discontinuous trait. Although each finger has a unique print, that uniqueness is attributable to tiny details which arise during a person's development from a fetus. Overall, the print on any finger can be classified as one of three possible patterns: **arches**, **loops**, and **whorls**.

The arch is the simplest pattern and is rare. Loops are the most common. The vast majority of loops are described as ulnar – that is, the base of the loop opens toward the little finger of the hand. The other kind of loop, opening towards the thumb, is called radial. Whorls are circular and are more common than arches but not as common as loops.

Loops and whorls are complex patterns. Each has a core at the center of the circular region, and a **triradius** outside the loop or whorl. The triradius is a point where the ridges from three different directions come together in a triangular pattern. A whorl actually has two triradii, one on each side.

Figure 2.3   Fingerprint types

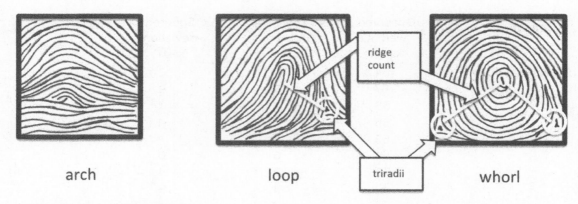

arch   loop   whorl

Fingerprint drawings by John Dickerman

In this exercise you will classify the fingerprints of each of your fingers and we will total up the distribution for the entire class. We will then examine the data in relation to a second discontinuous trait, the sex of the individual reporting each type of pattern.

1.   Color an area on a piece of scratch paper darkly with a #2 pencil.
2.   Examine your fingertip and look for the locations of the core and the triradii. It is critical that you include these points in your fingerprints. Rub that part of your fingertip on your colored scratch paper to darken the fingerprint.
3.   Take a piece of clear tape and place it on your fingerprint to pick up the graphite image. Again, be sure that you get the core and triradii. Transfer the tape to an index card and label which finger it came from. Repeat for each finger.
4.   Classify each print as arch, ulnar loop, radial loop, or whorl. You may need to look at the prints with a dissecting microscope to see them well.
5.   Your lab instructor will tally the distribution of each pattern, by sex, for the whole class in a two-dimensional table. Are the patterns distributed differently among the sexes?
6.   Construct a bar graph of the data.

Investigation #2   Measuring continuous variation in human fingerprints

The pattern of a fingerprint is a qualitative discontinuous trait. A different aspect of the print is quantitative and continuous: the number of ridges present. For each print, the ridge count is defined as the number of ridges between the core and the triradius. Arches, which have no triradius, always have a ridge count of zero. On the other hand, whorls have two triradii, so they have two possible values. By convention, the higher number is taken as the ridge count.

In figure 2.3, a white line has been superimposed between the core and the triradius of the loop and whorl patterns so that you can see where the ridge count is made. This loop has eleven ridges broken by this line, illustrating a ridge count of 11. The whorl shows a ridge count of 10 to the right triradius and a count of 13 to the left. Since the count towards the left is larger, the count of this print is taken as 13.

The **total ridge count** is the sum of the ridge count for all ten fingers. The genetics of total ridge counts is poorly understood, but the trait appears to be influenced by several genes.

1.   Determine the ridge count for each fingerprint on your card. Add them up to obtain the total ridge count.
2.   Your lab instructor will add these data to the class tally. Determine the average and standard deviation for male and female total ridge counts. Is there a difference by sex?

Investigation #3   Measuring continuous variation in beans

1.   You will be given a sample of pinto beans and lima beans. Measure the length and width of each bean with calipers and record the data. (These measurements may seem tedious but such detailed analyses are how biologists like paleontologists are able to sort bones and teeth or other specimens into different species.) Be sure to record the length and width of each bean – you will need to know which length goes with which width in step 4.
2.   Calculate the mean, variance, and standard deviation for each dimension of each bean. Draw histograms for the length and width of each bean, rounding off to the nearest mm.
3.   How do the standard deviations for the data from the measurements compare? Is the magnitude of the standard deviation related to the size of the associated mean? Calculate the **coefficient of variance** to correct the standard deviations for the size of the means:

$$V = s / \bar{x}$$

4.   Construct a two-dimensional frequency distribution by graphing the length versus the width of each bean. Plot both types of beans on the same graph, using different colors or symbols for the two kinds of beans. Does the variability (indicated by the size of the area of the graph in which data points appear) grow larger as the data values grow larger? (That is, are the points for the large beans more spread out than those for the small beans?)

A Selection Problem

Using your data from investigation number 3, work through the following simulation. You may use data from either the lima or pinto beans.

●   Assume that you are trying to breed a bigger bean and will only plant those beans that are larger than the mean length.
●   For the purposes of this problem, assume that the average length of the next generation will be 1 standard deviation larger than the population you started with. Also assume that the coefficient of variation will be the same (this means that the standard deviation will be bigger). Calculate what this would be.

- Repeat the process generation after generation, until you get a population whose mean length is at least twice that of the original population. How many generations did this change take?

Example:

33 beans are measured.

$\bar{x}$ = 12.5 mm
s = 1.1 mm
V = 0.09 (i.e., 9%)

Generation 2 would be:

$\bar{x}_2$ = 12.5 + 1.1 = 13.6

s_2 = 13.6 × 0.09 = 1.2

Generation 3 would be:

$\bar{x}_3$ = 13.6 + 1.2 = 14.8

s_3 = 14.8 × 0.09 = 1.3

etc.

Important Terms

arch
coefficient of variance
continuous trait
degrees of freedom
discontinuous trait
frequency distribution
histogram
loop
mean
natural selection
normal curve
standard deviation
statistics
total ridge count
triradius
variance
whorl

CHAPTER 3
SELECTION vs. GENETIC DRIFT

INTRODUCTION

No population can grow forever – sooner or later it will run out of food, space, or other resources and its members will begin to die off. Darwin's theory of natural selection predicts that, given the normal amount of variation present in a population, some individuals will be better able to survive and reproduce than others. The genes of the survivors will therefore become more common in the population over time. The converse of this idea is contained in the Hardy-Weinberg theorem – namely, in a population in which selection does not occur, alleles will be shuffled randomly but will not change in relative frequencies, and will remain generation after generation at the levels predicted by the Hardy-Weinberg equation.

In the 1930's, a geneticist named Sewell Wright analyzed the theory of natural selection using the mathematics of probability theory. He concluded that in reality natural selection could not be the only factor causing a population to change over time – when a population is very small, an element of randomness enters the picture which can result in the occasional replacement of one gene by another regardless of their relative effects on fitness. He called this random process **genetic drift**. The sizes of all populations are limited by their environments, so genetic drift is a real possibility and must be studied alongside natural selection. Since Wright published his theory there has been increasing interest among evolutionary biologists in determining how much evolution is due to increasing fitness and how much is due to random events.

SAMPLING ERROR

The tendency for the frequency of a given allele to drift in a population depends upon the population's size. Probability theory provides a mathematical explanation for this which is easily illustrated by an analogy. Imagine we have a large bowl of beads, half of which are red and half of which are white. If we pull one bead from the bowl at random, the probability that it will be red is 0.5. By extension, if we pull several beads from the bowl at random, we would expect 50% of them to be red. However, because the beads are removed at random, we will often find that the number of reds is a few more or a few less than half. When the actual fraction of reds differs from the expected 0.5, a **sampling error** has occurred. A sampling error is **not** a <u>mistake</u> in the sampling process – it is simply a normal deviation of a random sample from its theoretically expected value. Such deviations will occur from time to time no matter how carefully a sample is taken.

Figure 3.1. Frequency of various outcomes sampling beads four at a time.

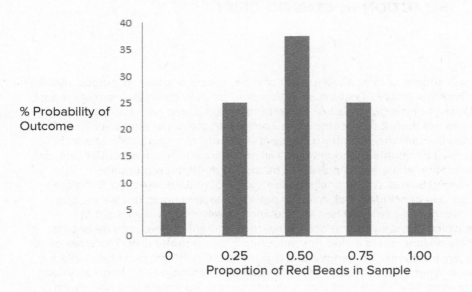

If we pull four beads from the bowl, the proportion of red beads we observe in our sample will be one of five possibilities: 0% (no reds), 25% (one red), 50% (two reds), 75% (three reds), or 100% (four reds). A proportion of 50% is the single most likely outcome since it is most representative of the whole bowl of beads. While the other possibilities are less likely, they will still occur in a certain percentage of samples. We can calculate the probabilities of these other possibilities occurring by using the binomial expansion series from probability theory. In this example, the probability of pulling out exactly two red beads and two white beads is 0.375. The remaining 62.5% of the time we would actually get something other than a 50-50 mix: 25% of the time there would be three reds, 25% of the time there would be one red, 6.25% of the time there would be four reds, and 6.25% of the time there would be no reds. This frequency distribution is graphed in figure 3.1 (note that the x-axis shows the proportion of reds rather than the actual number obtained in the sample).

A larger sample size gives a different distribution. Figure 3.2 shows the frequency distribution of the expected outcomes from pulling a sample of 50 beads from the bowl. (The y-axis of this graph has been expanded relative to that of figure 3.1 to allow for greater precision.)

Selection vs. Genetic Drift

Figure 3.2. Frequency of various outcomes sampling beads fifty at a time.

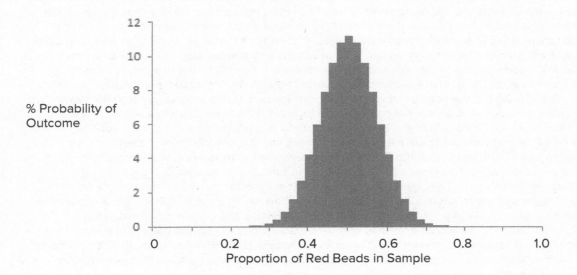

When fifty beads are sampled from the bowl, we still expect half of them (i.e., 25 beads) to be red. Note the difference in the shape of the distribution of possible outcomes, however. The distribution is much narrower when 50 beads are removed than when only four are removed. This indicates that there is less variance in the outcomes. The standard deviation for the first distribution was 0.255, but for the second it drops to 0.071. The magnitude of the standard deviations is proportional to the amount of sampling error that is likely to occur. We can see how much the sampling error drops with increasing sample size by noting that there is a 6.25% chance of getting all red beads when only four are removed, but when 50 beads are removed, the chance of them being all red plummets to 0.000 000 000 000 09%. This is, of course, consistent with the common sense notion that a large sample is much more likely to be representative of the whole than a small sample.

GENETIC DRIFT AS SAMPLING ERROR

Every generation the genes in a population go through a sampling process analogous to our bowl of beads. Instead of colored beads, let's shift our attention to two strains of flowers, one with red petals and one with white. Red petals are caused by the "red" allele and white petals are caused by the "white" allele (in order to keep this analogy simple, we will ignore the effects of dominance and heterozygosity). Our total population of genes will consist of all of the red and white alleles in all of the gametes in all of the flowers of our plants. Since each flower can produce hundreds of gametes, this population is very large. However, only some of these gametes will meet and form seeds, and only some seeds will germinate and grow into adult plants, so the next generation is equivalent to just a sample of this generation's population of alleles. If the red allele is present in the original population at a frequency of 0.5, then we would expect it to be present in the next generation at a frequency of 0.5. However, since the next generation is but a sample of the first, sampling error will mean that the frequency of the red allele probably will not be exactly 0.5. If each generation is large (i.e., all available seeds are planted and raised to maturity), then the error should be small and the frequency of the red allele will stay close to 0.5. But if the population of second generation plants is small (like a garden), then a substantial deviation from the original allele frequency is quite possible.

Let's assume these flowers are being maintained in a tiny plot just big enough to hold about 10 plants. Each year they are allowed to go to seed and whatever comes up in the spring will be the next generation of flowers. The gardener thins the plants down to 10 each summer, but does so before they flower so she cannot select for flower color. Suppose that we determine one year that the frequency of the gene that codes for a red flower is 0.60, and that the alternate allele that codes for a white flower has a frequency of 0.40. Each flower will produce pollen and ovules, 60% of which carry the red gene and 40% of which carry the white gene. Pollination occurs at random and the seeds mature and fall to the ground. In the spring, some of them germinate, but only 10 are allowed to grow and flower. We would expect that the frequency of the red gene is still 0.60 but we may find that, by random chance, it has changed, say to 0.48. When this second generation reproduces, it will form a gamete pool in which 48% of the gametes will carry the red gene and 52% will carry the white. When the third generation forms, we would expect the frequency of the red gene to be 0.48, but by random chance it may be different, say 0.67. In the fourth generation we may find the frequency to be 0.75 and in the fifth 0.72. Every generation the frequency of the red allele shifts from that of the previous generation by sampling error, and, in turn, <u>the frequency of the gene in the gamete pool that will make up the next generation reflects this shift</u>. After many generations we may find the frequency of the red allele to have drifted up and down as seen in figure 3.3. Notice that at generation 39, the frequency of the red allele goes to zero. At this point the white allele becomes **fixed** in the population. The population has evolved from one of mixed color to one of uniform color. Yet this has not happened because red flowers are inferior to white. In fact, under genetic drift the white allele could have just as easily disappeared. What happened was that the population size was so small that genetic drift prevented the maintenance of the Hardy-Weinberg equilibrium.

Figure 3.3. Changing frequency of allele for red flowers in a hypothetical population

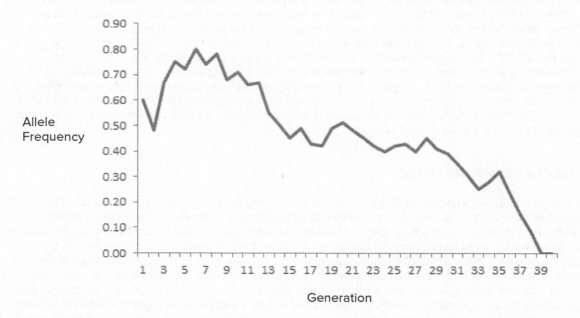

Given enough time, fixation of one allele over another would be an inevitable result of genetic drift (unless opposed by sufficiently strong selection or mutation pressure). The only case in which fixation would never occur is when population size is infinite. Since all populations are considerably smaller than this, drift must be a force in evolution to some extent. In a very large population (N > 10,000), drift is small, and the number of generations needed to fix an allele by drift may be more than the average number of generations that a species exists on earth. In a small population (N < 100), drift can be large, and hence fixation rapid. The number of generations needed for an allele to become fixed in a population by drift is thus proportional to population size. This is one reason biologists are so concerned about the genetic diversity of endangered species.

SELECTION AND DRIFT

It is possible for a gene frequency to be simultaneously affected by both genetic drift and natural selection. Suppose that in the flower example above the red flowers were more attractive to pollinating bees and thus were more likely to produce seeds. Under these conditions, and when population size is large, the red allele will become fixed at a predictable rate that is proportional to the allele's effect on reproduction. Under the same conditions, but when population size is small, both genetic drift and selection will be acting, and the rate at which the red allele becomes fixed is less predictable. If population size is very small, drift will occasionally overcome selection, even when the selective advantage of the allele is huge.

INVESTIGATIONS WITH GENETIC DRIFT

In this lab you will use the bowl of beads analogy to do three exercises exploring the properties of genetic drift. The first two demonstrate the effect of population size on drift, and the third simulates a case in which drift and selection both operate.

Investigation #1   Drift in a small population
Simulate the drift in a population of two individuals. Each individual requires two gametes, so the sample size is four.
1.   Pull four beans from a jar to represent the gametes which form the two individuals. For the first generation, start at the 50/50 jar, pull 4 beans, and count the number of white beans. Replace the beans in the 50/50 jar.
2.   If there were two white beans, simulate the next generation by drawing four more beans from the 50/50 jar. If there were three white beans in your sample, then use the 75/25 jar for the next generation; if there was one white bean, use the 25/75 jar, etc. For each generation use the jar which reflects the ratio of white to colored beans in the previous generation. Always return the beans to the jar they came from so the jar's population does not change.
3.   Record the ratio of white to colored beans for every generation, and continue until all the beans in a sample are of one color (that is, the "allele" is fixed). Do this exercise twice.
4.   Graph the results of these exercises as a plot of the frequency of the white "allele" at successive generations (cf. figure 3.3). Plot both trials on a single axis. Do they both fix on the same color "allele"?
5.   Compare your results with those obtained by the rest of the class. What percentage of trials did the process fix on white and what percentage on colored? How does this compare to the original 50/50 starting conditions?

Investigation #2   Drift in a large population
Follow the same procedure as in exercise 1, but this time simulate 5 individuals by pulling out 10 beans. Use the appropriate set of jars for this exercise, as there are more potential ratios which can occur in this exercise. Do this exercise twice and plot the results as before. How does this compare to the small population? Compare your results to the class as before. Is there a difference as to how quickly a given "allele" gets fixed when the population size increases?

Investigation #3   Drift and selection

Follow the procedure for exercise 2, only use the bowls filled with different sized beans instead of the colored beans. Do this exercise twice and graph the results. Compare your results to the class. Is there consistent evidence of selection? Judging by the number of generations needed for fixation, is the "selection pressure" large or small? Would this influence the relative importance of selection versus drift?

Important Terms

fixation
genetic drift
sampling error

CHAPTER 4
INTRODUCTION TO BIOLOGICAL DIVERSITY

WHY STUDY DIVERSITY?

As humans transform larger and larger areas of the earth, concern for biodiversity grows. Yet few people properly appreciate the incredible diversity of creatures which live on this planet. Consider, for example, that even if you were to examine 100,000 different organisms every week for an entire semester (that comes to 10 each <u>second</u> for your 3-hour lab period!) you would only have enough time to encounter the known species of insects. There would be no time left to see the millions of species of insects which probably exist but have not yet been cataloged, let alone other types of animals, plants, fungi, or bacteria.

With so many different organisms to study, you may wonder why anyone would even bother to try. What is the point of describing over a million insect species, collecting hundreds of thousands of different flowers, or naming fifty thousand species of snails?

- Many people study organisms because they find them fascinating. This level of interest may seem odd to other people, but it is important, for without such motivation no one would be willing to do the painstaking work necessary to sort out the millions of kinds of life on earth and study them at all. And it is not just professional biologists who are attracted to the study of organisms; the famous Russian-American novelist Vladimir Nabokov, for example, was an expert on butterflies and traveled the world to see them.

- Medical doctors, who like to concentrate on the study of human anatomy and physiology, also benefit from studying bacteria, protozoa, fungi, and parasitic worms. All of these creatures can cause diseases, and anyone interested in medicine must have some knowledge of them and how they interact with other species.

- Many medicinal compounds come from plants, fungi, and other organisms. For example, antibiotics are isolated from molds and bacteria. Some of the earliest attempts at biological classification were the medieval books called herbals that were intended to organize what was known about medicinal plants. Indeed, one of the major fears about declining biodiversity is that we will forever lose valuable medicines as various plants become extinct.

- The ecological interactions between the earth's creatures are also important. This was underscored several years ago when engineers tried to build a small, totally enclosed environment for people to live in, in part as a prelude to designing artificial habitats in space. Their artificial ecosystem quickly collapsed and the inhabitants had to be evacuated because the enclosure did not include enough microbial diversity to keep the air and water clean. Similarly, changing the biodiversity in natural environments can also have dire effects on their habitability. We still have only a poor understanding of how materials get recycled in nature.

- The study of evolutionary history also depends on an accurate knowledge of existing biodiversity. Again, scientists tend to explore evolution because of professional curiosity, but this work does have practical implications. For example, the evolutionary distance between bacteria and people is so great that it is not too difficult to develop drugs that can kill bacteria without harming people. It is somewhat harder to treat fungal infections safely, and can be even more difficult to treat infestations of parasitic animals. Establishing how related organisms are and exactly how they differ can help people design new antibiotics and pesticides.

In the chapters which follow, evolutionary relationships will be stressed in order to place our survey of organisms within the context of a coherent narrative. This approach is not intended to slight the many other reasons for studying biodiversity, it simply helps us to organize what would otherwise be an impossibly huge task.

It is clearly impossible to look at thousands of species every week, or even all semester. In the following chapters we will focus on a few representative creatures which effectively illustrate large groups of organisms. It is possible to make valid generalizations about these groups because biologists have spent the last three centuries trying to organize everything they know about living creatures into an organized framework. This complex organization is the product of a discipline called **systematics.**

SYSTEMATICS

A population (or group of populations) of individuals capable of interbreeding is called a **species**. Biologists make detailed descriptions of the species they study and group them with similar species. These groups are put together with similar groups to form larger groups, and so all known organisms are classified in a regular, or systematic, way. The science of systematics therefore includes both the study of diversity and the process of making sense of that diversity. One subdiscipline of systematics is **taxonomy,** the actual process of naming and classifying individual species. The other subdiscipline of systematics is **phylogentetics**, which is the science of reconstructing evolutionary history and relationships. Even though the term *systematics* encompasses a broader range of activity than the term *taxonomy*, they are sometimes used interchangeably.

Classification systems are not always easy to make. Moreover, it is possible for two different scientists to look at the same data and come up with different classifications. The guiding principle of systematics is that a classification system should be useful. That is, it should help us organize our knowledge in a reasonable way so that we can make accurate generalizations or predictions based on what we know.

Say, for example, that you lived your whole life in the desert and only knew about the plants and animals found there. You come across a reference to the dandelion, whose scientific name is *Taraxacum officinale*. From the common name you might think that this creature is some kind of lion, but if you read further that it is a member of the plant kingdom, you could compare it to the plants that you know and deduce that it is photosynthetic and has a characteristic pattern of growth (characteristics of plants are listed in chapter 9). Learning that *Taraxacum* belongs to Division Anthophyta of the plant kingdom (see chapter 10), you could predict further that it is a vascular plant that produces flowers and seeds. Knowing that it belongs to Order Eudicotyledones would tell you something about its embryology and internal structure, while finding it in the family Asteraceae would indicate that its flowers are arranged in special clusters called capitulums (cf. chapter 10). Thus by knowing where *Taraxacum officinale* fits into a classification scheme, you can deduce much about it without ever having seen an example of the species. As you continue to study biology in future courses, you will often come across references to groups of organisms. If a physiologist were to tell you that flatworms excrete waste nitrogen as urea while gastropods excrete uric acid, the statement would make no sense to you unless you knew what flatworms and gastropods were. Knowledge of phylogenetics also helps scientists choose appropriate organisms for particular experiments – if we want to generalize from the data obtained with one organism, we need to know what is related to it and what is not.

The first attempts at classification were crude and not very systematic. Organisms were grouped according to easily observable characteristics: Plants were either trees, vines, or shrubs; animals either swam, crawled, or flew. In the 18th century Carolus Linnaeus developed a new system for classifying plants. His method was artificial – he merely counted flower parts and grouped them accordingly (e.g., plants with

2 stamens, plants with 3 stamens, etc.) – but it was very systematic. Linnaeus constructed a hierarchy of categories which, but with few modifications, is still used today:

        Kingdom
            Phylum (or Division)
               Class
                 Order
                   Family
                     Genus
                       Species

Thus, each kingdom is made of several phyla, each phylum is made of one or more classes, and so on. Any particular group (e.g., the plant kingdom, the ape family) is called a **taxon.**

Furthermore, Linnaeus popularized a practice (actually begun by the Swiss botanist Gaspard Bauhin) of referring to each species by a **binomial** – a generic name and a specific epithet. A genus is a broad type of organism. For example, all oak trees belong to the genus *Quercus*. Within that generic group of oaks, there are dozens of specific types: white oaks, red oaks, pin oaks, etc. Each of these is a species of oak (e.g., white oaks are *Quercus alba*, red oaks are *Quercus rubra*, etc.). In the example of the dandelion cited above, *Taraxacum* is the name of its genus, and *officinale* the specific epithet. (Genus and species names are <u>always</u> underlined or italicized. The generic name is also capitalized.) These scientific names are unique to each species and allow any organism to be identified unambiguously.

In the last 200 years biologists have tried to make taxonomy less artificial and more based on overall similarities of form. Moreover, since Darwin first proposed the theory of evolution by natural selection, it has been realized that, ideally, a classification should reflect evolutionary relationships. Consider the following table illustrating the classification of three animals:

	Turtle	Dog	Cat
Kingdom	Animalia	Animalia	Animalia
Phylum	Chordata	Chordata	Chordata
Class	Reptilia	Mammalia	Mammalia
Order	Testudinata	Carnivora	Carnivora
Family	Emydidae	Canidae	Felidae
Genus	*Terrapene*	*Canis*	*Felis*
Species	*Terrapene carolina*	*Canis familiaris*	*Felis cattus*

As a natural classification system, this table shows which animals are similar and which are not. Since cats and dogs are more like each other than they are like turtles, they are placed in the same order (Carnivora) and turtles are excluded. However, this scheme is also based on phylogenetic research, so it reflects current ideas about evolutionary descent. The fossil record indicates that cats and dogs are modern variants of a single ancestral species that lived millions of years ago. This ancient species was the first carnivore. The turtle also shares a common ancestor with the dog and cat, but one much more distant: the ancestor of all modern chordates.

HOMOLOGY vs. ANALOGY

Although it is possible to observe evolution directly (for example, in experiments like those in chapter 1), it is, of course, impossible to directly observe speciation events which occurred millions of years ago. In order to reconstruct phylogenetic history biologists look for **homologous structures.** Homologous structures are different structures that exhibit internal similarities so striking that they suggest a common evolutionary origin. For example, turtles, dogs, and cats all possess a dorsal nerve cord that is the basis for their central nervous systems. This structure, while differing slightly from species to species, is so complex that it is unlikely to have evolved more than once. This is what we mean when we say that these animals all evolved from an ancestral chordate – they all developed from the first species that had this kind of nerve cord.

Determining what is a homology is not simple. A structure may become highly modified by **divergent evolution** as a population adapts to a new environment. One example of divergent evolution can be seen by comparing a bird's wing to a human arm. The wing and the arm perform different functions and appear to be quite different. Inside, however, both limbs contain the same bones in a similar arrangement. Many of the wing bones are fused to form sturdy supports for the powerful flight muscles, yet the underlying pattern matches that of the arm bones. Evolutionary theory seeks to explain this structural parallel by postulating that both birds and humans are descendants of an animal that had this basic limb bone arrangement. Over hundreds of millions of years, this ancestral animal's descendents slowly changed in different ways and the forms of the limbs diverged. In one group the limb bones grew together into a wing, in another they lengthened into the human arm. Indeed, the observable fact that some wing bones are actually formed of several smaller bones fused together would be difficult to explain in any other way.

On the other hand, **analogous structures** can also confuse the issue. These are structures which appear similar but upon closer inspection turn out to be quite unrelated. They represent adaptations of diverse creatures to similar environments. Like a bird's wing, a butterfly wing is flat and strong to power flight. Unlike the bird wing, the butterfly wing contains no bones and is, in fact, an outgrowth of the butterfly's hard exoskeleton, which has no homolog in the bird at all. The two types of wing are actually different methods for flying molded by the laws of aerodynamics into similar shapes. The process of adaptation that causes different structures to assume similar forms in order to perform similar functions is called **convergent evolution.**

Homology and analogy are difficult concepts and non-biologists often fall into a trap of circular reasoning when discussing them. It may seem simple to say that bird and butterfly wings are analogous because birds and butterflies evolved from different ancestors, but such a statement is backwards. The wings are analogous because they are structurally different, and from this we deduce that birds and butterflies evolved from different ancestors. Homologies and analogies are defined strictly in terms of similar and dissimilar structures. In fact, the idea of homologous and analogous structures predates Darwin's theory; evolution explains why they occur as they do.

CLADISTICS

A model of phylogentic descent is often expressed graphically as a tree rooted in an ancestral species and branching out to the various species descended from that ancestor. A powerful method for building trees is to focus on specific changes in the homologous structures found in related species.

In the method of **cladistics**, the presence or absence of homologs, and how they may have changed through history, is analyzed with mathematical rigor. The various traits of the organisms are studied in detail to determine which are ancestral (that is, like the traits of the ancestral species) and which are derived (modified from the ancestral condition). Shared derived characters – that is, modified traits common to a particular group of species – tell us how the ancestral tree branched during history.

Increasingly, systematists are trying to base classification systems on the branching patterns of cladistic trees. A key principle of cladistics is that a valid taxon shoud be equivalent to a section of a tree that includes an ancestor and all of its descendants. Such a section of a tree is called a **clade**. Cladistic analysis sometimes challenges traditional notions of a taxon. For example, if we say that Class Reptilia should include the ancestral reptile with all of its descendants, then the class would include birds, which descended from dinosaurs. Thinking of birds as feathered reptiles may seem strange, but it is a view now shared by most biologists. We shall see that many areas of classification are not at all settled.

Important Terms

analogous structure
binomial
clade
cladistics
convergent evolution
divergent evolution
homologous structure
phylogenetic
species
systematics
taxon
taxonomy

CHAPTER 5
THE DOMAINS OF LIFE
PART I: THE PROKARYOTIC DOMAINS

INTRODUCTION

Under the microscope bacteria are small and simple. Yet in many respects bacteria are the single most diverse group of organisms on earth. Prokaryotes were the only form of life for most of our planet's history, existing 2,000,000,000 years before the first eukaryote and 3,000,000,000 years before the appearance of anything remotely familiar to us today. During this time prokaryotes reproduced and adapted relentlessly, colonizing every part of the earth. Living microbes have even been found in volcanic steam vents at the bottom of the ocean and sealed in sedimentary rocks hundreds of feet below the earth's surface.

Figure 5.1. Fossil history of life

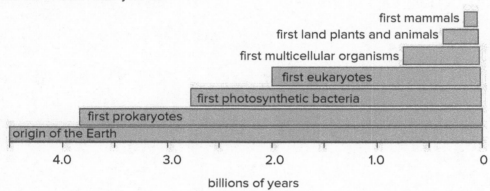

In the previous chapter we said that it was useful to classify organisms in order to systematize what we know about them. This is especially true for bacteria, because they are such a complex group. Microbiologists have for years used a classification system based on the results different species of bacteria give to various chemical tests. This system has indeed been useful in categorizing bacteria that cause disease, contaminate food, or otherwise influence human affairs. Unfortunately, this system is not phylogenetic, since it is not based on any knowledge of bacterial evolution – the tests are too simple to differentiate homologous from analogous metabolic processes.

Bacterial taxonomy began to change in the late 1970's when molecular biologists learned how to sequence DNA. This made it possible to directly study an organism's genetic material and compare it to that of another species, revealing how genetic changes had accumulated over the years as species diverged. The genetic code can be used to tell whether molecules (such as enzymes or ribosomal subunits) from different species are homologous or not. One of the first discoveries from this approach, made by Carl Woese at the University of Illinois, was the most astounding – there were actually two completely different kinds of prokaryotes. These two groups of prokaryotes are so different genetically and chemically that they must have diverged billions of years ago, before eukaryotes even existed.

One of the groups that Woese identified tended to come from exotic habitats such as boiling mineral springs, extremely salty water, and other unusual places. Many of these environments have little or no oxygen, and the prokaryotes that live there cannot survive in environments that we would consider "normal." Woese called them **archaea** because they appeared to be the modern representatives of a line of evolution that has changed little since life began. Because archaea live in environments that are difficult to replicate in the lab, we will not be able to work with them very much in this class.

We will concentrate instead on the **bacteria**, a large and diverse group of organisms that includes most well-known prokaryotes. Although they do not thrive in the bizarre places favored by the archaea, bacteria are ubiquitous in any place familiar to humans.

Woese found that archaea and bacteria are so different that, compared to them, all eukaryotes seem pretty similar, at least as far as their DNA is concerned. Since Woese is a molecular biologist, he suggested changing taxonomy to reflect these molecular differences and first proposed the term **domain** as a taxon larger than a kingdom to facilitate the new taxonomy. Woese said there should be three domains: **Archaea**, **Bacteria**, and **Eukarya** (all eukaryotes). This system has been adopted by most biologists, although it is not always clear how to divide the domains into kingdoms.

MODERN ARCHAEA

The best known archaea live in very harsh environments. **Halophiles** live in evaporation ponds so salty that they would pickle any other kind of organism (*hals* is Greek for salt, *philos* Greek for loving, hence "salt-loving") **Thermophiles** live at temperatures close to (or sometimes even exceeding) boiling, conditions found in hot springs and underwater volcanoes. Oftentimes these environments are very acidic as well. Although either acid or extreme heat by itself would kill almost any eukaryote, the thermophiles seem to be more closely related to eukaryotes than any other prokaryote. (In fact, complex eukaryotic chromosomes may be a variation on a trick thermophiles use to keep their DNA from melting.) A third large group of archaea are the **methanogens**, creatures that generate methane gas as a by-product of their metabolism. Many archaea cannot grow in the presence of oxygen, suggesting that this group was well established before oxygen became plentiful 2.5 billion years ago. In recent years it has become clear that archaea are also common in more mundane environments, but their culture conditions still have not been worked out very well, so even these more accessible species are hard to grow in the lab for now.

CULTURING BACTERIA

Bacteria were first observed microscopically in the 17th century, although it turns out that people had been unwittingly growing bacteria in products like yogurt, cheese, and vinegar for thousands of years. Even so, they were not grown under defined conditions in the laboratory until the 19th century. When we speak of bacterial growth, we really mean an increase in the number of individuals – the size of a bacterial cell does not change much except when the cell divides to form daughter cells. A mass of bacterial cells derived from a single cell is called a **colony**.

The wide distribution of bacteria means that samples of them are easy to come by. On the other hand, any given sample is likely to contain many different species of bacteria. For detailed study it is best to isolate bacteria into pure **cultures** and grow them separately. Isolating bacteria and keeping them free from contamination require special techniques.

Bacteria must grow on some type of **medium**. Media are solutions of nutrients which the bacteria can use for growth. There are hundreds of kinds of media to meet the individual needs of various species – no single medium will work for every kind of bacteria. In fact, there are many species of bacteria which have been detected in nature but that have never been cultured in the laboratory because a suitable medium was not available.

One of the factors that determines what nutrients go into a particular medium is the carbon source that the organism being cultured requires. Most species (including humans and other animals) are **heterotrophic** – they obtain their carbon from carbohydrates, fats, or other organic molecules in the food they consume. Therefore media for heterotrophic bacteria must contain some kind of organic substance that the organism can digest. On the other hand, some organisms can manufacture their own organic molecules from carbon dioxide taken directly from the environment. Such creatures are termed **autotrophic**. Media for autotrophs are often very simple since the organism makes most of what it needs by itself. Strictly speaking, heterotrophy and autotrophy refer specifically to how a creature obtains its carbon, but often the terms are used to describe an organism's energy source as well. That's because most heterotrophs obtain energy when they digest organic molecules (as when humans eat fat or sugar) while most autotrophs obtain their energy from the sun. Some bacteria are exceptions to this rule (e.g., chemoautotrophs use carbon dioxide for carbon but obtain energy from inorganic substances like iron or sulfur instead of the sun), but they are rare. Photosynthetic autotrophs are common enough to inspire their own special name, as they are sometimes called **phototrophs**.

Media can be liquid or gelled with a starch-like substance called **agar**. A liquid nutrient medium is called **broth**. The medium we will use the most is a pretty basic recipe and is simply called **nutrient broth**. When gelled, it is called **nutrient agar**. Agar poured into a shallow petri dish is called a **plate**.

Since there are bacteria virtually everywhere, care must be taken lest the cultures you are interested in become contaminated. Contamination can be prevented with proper **aseptic technique**. This involves using carefully sterilized media and instruments to handle cultures.

The most common way to sterilize materials is by **autoclaving**. An autoclave is essentially a giant pressure-cooker that uses super-heated steam at high pressure to destroy any cells present on objects placed inside it. Once autoclaved, a sealed vessel will remain sterile until opened. When culture vessels are opened, their mouths are flamed with a bunsen burner. This heats the air inside the vessel, creating air currents which prevent contaminated air from entering. Small instruments can be sterilized at the lab bench as you need them. **Inoculating loops**, used to transfer small amounts of bacteria from one medium to another, are designed to be flamed to red-hot temperatures before contacting a pure culture. Other instruments, such as forceps or glass rods, must be dipped in alcohol and ignited to be sterilized.

BACTERIAL MORPHOLOGY

Bacterial colonies can differ in color, texture, and odor. And although prokaryotic cells do not contain all of the complex organelles that eukaryotic cells do, they can still be differentiated to some extent under the microscope. Bacterial species can vary in shape, and the patterns in which bacterial cells may stick together can be distinctive. While none of these attributes is, by itself, sufficient to unambiguously identify a given bacterial species, microscopic examination of a species' cellular form is an important step in studying any bacterial specimen.

Most bacteria have one of three common shapes: spheres (**cocci**), rods (**bacilli**), or spirals (known as both **spirilla** and **spirochetes**). Some species grow in particular clusters or arrangements of cells, and this can also be used to describe the species. For example, a string of cocci is called **streptococcus**, and a cluster of cocci is called **staphylococcus**. The most common shapes and arrangements are shown in figure 5.2.

Figure 5.2. Bacterial shapes and arrangements

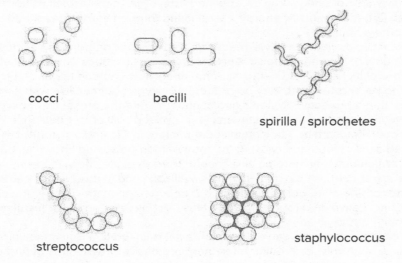

cocci

bacilli

spirilla / spirochetes

streptococcus

staphylococcus

The shape of a bacterium does not change. Therefore, shape is a useful characteristic for identifying bacterial species. The names of bacterial species often reflect this, and that can be confusing. For example, all members of the genus *Bacillus* are bacilli, but not every bacillus is a member of *Bacillus* – *Clostridium*, *Escherichia*, *Klebsiella*, *Pseudomonas*, and *Salmonella*, among many others, are all genera of bacilli. Similarly, *Streptococcus* and *Staphylococcus* are the names of genera as well as terms for arrangements. In this chapter you will work with species from some of these genera. How can you tell whether a written reference is to the shape or to the genus?

BACTERIAL METABOLISM: SAPROTROPHY, OXYGEN, AND FERMENTATION

Given the thousands of kinds of bacteria that exist in the world, it would be difficult to tell them all apart simply by cell and colony morphology. Bacteria are diverse not because of their structures but because of their abilities to live in different environments and use different sources of energy and nutrition. Most bacteria are heterotrophs, so many identification tests for bacteria involve growing them on media with different carbon sources (e.g., lactose vs. glucose) to see which they can survive on. Information can also be gained on exactly how the organism obtains its food.

Heterotrophs have essentially three ways of obtaining food. Most animals ingest their food but this option is not open to bacteria – their small size and rigid cell walls prevent them from eating other organisms. Instead, many bacteria are **parasites**, living inside other organisms and absorbing nutrients at their host's expense. Parasitic species of bacteria are famous for causing diseases. The third option for heterotrophs is **saprotrophy**. Saprotrophs live off of dead or decaying matter. These organisms are found throughout the environment and are responsible for spoilage and decomposition. (This may seem like a disgusting way to live, but its importance cannot be overemphasized – imagine a world in which wastes and dead organisms simply piled up forever without ever being broken down and recycled!) The vast majority of bacteria are saprotrophs.

Saprotrophs have a big problem: They sit on top of their food (or in it) and must consume it without actually eating. The only way to do this is to digest the food while it is still outside their bodies and absorb the nutrition so released. This is accomplished by secreting **exoenzymes** into the food. In exercise #2 you will test some bacteria to see if they are able to make a particular exoenzyme that can digest starch.

Once absorbed, organic molecules still need to be processed inside the cell, especially if they are to release energy. Small amounts of energy can be obtained from organic molecules without using oxygen via glycolysis, but much larger amounts of energy are released through aerobic respiration. Some bacteria require oxygen while others do not.

Oxygen is a very reactive molecule and will readily degrade many compounds besides carbohydrates. As a result, excess amounts of oxygen are toxic. **Aerobic** organisms produce enzymes that can neutralize oxygen and thereby control its harmful side effects. Some **anaerobic** bacteria are also able to detoxify oxygen. They are said to be **aerotolerant**: they do not require oxygen but can live with it. However, some anaerobic bacteria lack these protective systems and cannot tolerate the presence of oxygen. These **obligate anaerobes** live in oxygen-poor environments (e.g., in deep soil) or in media that are somehow separated from the normal atmosphere. For example, the bacterium *Clostridium botulinum* is famous for living in vacuum-packed cans of food and causing the form of food poisoning known as botulism. Other organisms are able to switch between aerobic and anaerobic ways of life. More than simply aerotolerant, **facultative anaerobes** are able to use oxygen when it is available, and in its absence can still grow slowly as anaerobes. When discussing anaerobic organisms, it is important to state whether the creature is facultative or obligate. Facultative anaerobes are sometimes simply referred to as "facultative", but the word "anaerobe" is ambiguous by itself.

In the absence of oxygen, glycolysis can only continue if it is linked to a fermentative pathway that metabolizes the products of glycolysis. In eukaryotes there are basically two forms of fermentation: In animals, fermentation produces lactic acid; and in plants and fungi, fermentation produces ethanol and carbon dioxide. However, among anaerobic bacteria there are many other types of fermentation. The main product is an organic compound (usually, but not always, an acid) and some kinds of fermentation also produce a gas such as CO_2 or hydrogen. The ability of a bacterial species to ferment carbohydrates, and the kind of products such fermentation produces, can be used to help identify that species.

Bacterial fermentation is of considerable economic importance. For example, yogurt and cheese are formed when fermenting bacteria produce enough acid to curdle the milk they are grown in. If cheesemakers use a gas-forming bacterium, then their cheese will have bubbles in it (like Swiss cheese). Different species of bacteria produce different kinds of organic acids, and this greatly affects the flavor of the cheeses they make. Fermenting bacteria were discovered by Louis Pasteur, and sterilizing milk to protect it from going sour is called **pasteurization**. Other types of bacteria are used in a variety of industrial fermentation processes to produce all kinds of chemicals.

SYMBIOSIS AND NITROGEN FIXATION

Autotrophs create organic molecules out of CO_2 and water. But life depends on other elements besides carbon, oxygen, and hydrogen. Nitrogen is a critical ingredient of amino acids and nucleotides. The atmosphere is 78% nitrogen gas, but living organisms cannot incorporate atmospheric nitrogen into organic compounds directly. First it must be reduced to ammonia. This process, called **nitrogen fixation**, requires tremendous amounts of energy and is very difficult to do. Only a few genera of bacteria are able to fix nitrogen. Just as all life depends on autotrophs to make organic compounds out of carbon dioxide, the world also depends on nitrogen-fixing bacteria to make ammonia. The most powerful nitrogen-fixers tend to live in plant roots and "trade" their ammonia for some of the plant's carbohydrates. In essence, the photosynthesis of the plant supplies the energy for the bacterial nitrogen fixation. The bacteria form **nodules** of infected cells on the plant roots, but in this case the infection is helpful rather than harmful.

A situation in which individuals of two different species live closely together is called **symbiosis**. There are three different types of symbiotic relationships:

- the relationship may be harmful to one of the partners (**parasitism**)
- the relationship may benefit both partners (**mutualism**)
- the relationship may benefit one partner while the other is neither harmed nor helped (**commensalism**).

In practice, it can be difficult to determine whether a symbiont is being affected slightly or not at all, so commensal associations are hard to prove. Nitrogen-fixing bacterial root nodules are clearly mutualistic associations.

INVESTIGATIONS WITH BACTERIA

In order to allow time for the bacteria to grow, several of the following activities will be set up in one class period and evaluated in the next class period. For exercise #1 you will be sampling bacteria from the environment, but for the remaining exercises the following pure cultures will be available:

Bacillus megaterium
Escherichia coli
Enterococcus faecalis
Staphylococcus epidermidis

(Note: Scientific names can be abbreviated by using the initial of the genus and the specific epithet; e.g., *E. coli*.)

Because space for incubating cultures is limited, you will not perform all of the tests on all of the species – follow your instructor's directions. Be sure your materials are properly labeled with your name and section. Include the name of the organism inoculated onto each plate or tube.

Investigation #1   Isolating bacteria from the environment

In the following exercise, your lab instructor will give you and your partner a plate of sterile nutrient agar. You will use a sterile swab to inoculate the plate with microorganisms from the environment. With proper technique, you should be able to separate the different species you collect as individual colonies.

1. Decide what kind of environment you want to use as your source. This will determine the technique you use:
    (a) Dry surfaces (table top, leaf surface, skin, scalp, etc.)   Moisten the sterile swab in a tube of sterile water and squeeze it out against the side of the tube. Vigorously rub the wet swab over approximately 1 square inch of surface. If you are sampling an area far from the lab, carry the bacteria-laden swab back to the lab inside a dry sterile tube to prevent contamination.
    (b) Moist surfaces (throat, aquarium, etc.)   Rub the swab on the desired surface, but be gentle when dealing with human subjects!
    (c) Hair or clothing   Shake it over the surface of the agar (in this case, skip step 2).
    (d) Air   Take the lid off of the plate and expose it for an hour (in this case, skip step 2).
2. On the back of the plate to be inoculated, draw a line with a marking pencil to divide the plate in half. Inoculate the agar plate by streaking the swab back and forth across one half of the agar about 10 times. Discard the swab. Give the plate a quarter turn. Using a fresh sterile swab, streak across the first set of streaks in a direction perpendicular to the original streaks. Make about four streaks, then streak back and forth without touching the old streaks in order to fill the second half of the agar. (This technique is intended to dilute the number of bacteria so that there will be isolated colonies in at least one quarter of the surface.)
3. Place the plate where your instructor directs so the bacteria can grow before the next lab period. Store the plates upside down (that is, with the agar medium on top). This helps trap moisture inside the plate and keeps the medium from drying out too fast.

Figure 5.3. Environmental streaking

first streak

second streak

one week later
isolated colonies in the
fourth quadrant

Period Two

1. Examine your plate for individual colonies. In the heavily streaked areas the colonies will be crowded and hard to differentiate, so concentrate on the lighter areas. Your "cleanest" colonies should be in the last quadrant.
2. Colonies can be categorized by size, color, consistency, and shape. Identify as many <u>different</u> kinds of colonies as you can on your plate. Describe each in your notes. For each isolated colony record:

    color

    shape (circular, irregular, filamentous)

    consistency (soft, firm, dry, brittle, sticky)

    size (in mm)

    Are some kinds more common than others? This reflects the number of each type of bacteria in the original sample.

Investigation #2   Starch exoenzymes

Starch is a complex carbohydrate which, when digested, turns into smaller molecules of maltose. When stained with a solution of iodine/potassium iodide, starch turns a deep blue color; maltose does not. In the following test, you will grow bacteria on a plate containing starch agar. Those bacteria that can produce an exoenzyme to digest starch will produce an area on the plate where the starch has turned to sugar. These areas will remain clear when the plate is stained with iodine solution.

1. Obtain a starch agar plate. On the back of the plate, draw a line with a marking pencil to divide the plate in half. Label one side "<u>E</u>. <u>coli</u>", and the other "<u>B</u>. <u>meg</u>."
2. Flame a loop and aseptically transfer a loopful of *E. coli* to the middle of the appropriate region of the plate. <u>Do not spread the culture around</u> – <u>leave it in a small area</u>
3. Repeat step 2 for *B. megaterium*.
4. Place the plate where your instructor directs.

Period Two

1. Flood the plate with IKI solution.
2. Compare the results for *E. coli* and *B. megaterium*. Does either produce an exoenzyme for starch?

Investigation #3   Fermentation

Bacterial fermentation generally produces some kind of acid as a by-product, although the exact kind of acid depends on the species of bacteria and what kind of sugar is being fermented. Acids can be easily detected by acid-base indicators. One commonly used indicator is phenol red. Phenol red is red in neutral or basic solutions but turns yellow in the presence of acid. Therefore fermentation will turn a tube of phenol red broth yellow.

Sometimes a gas is also produced during fermentation. For this reason, phenol red tubes usually contain an small upside-down tube (called a Durham tube). That way, if gas is released, it will be trapped inside the Durham tube and be visible as a bubble.

There are three possible outcomes for this experiment: no fermentation, production of acid, or production of acid and gas. The class will therefore evaluate three different species: *B. megaterium*, *E. faecalis*, and *E. coli*. You and your partner will be assigned to do one of these.

1. Flame an inoculating loop to red-hot. As the loop cools, remove the caps from a sterile phenol red tube and one of the culture tubes of bacteria. Pass the mouths of both tubes through the flame. Dip the loop into the broth culture and then inoculate the phenol red.
2. Flame both tubes again and replace the caps. Flame your loop when you are done.

Period Two
1. Examine the tube for signs of fermentation. Determine whether or not your specimen can ferment, and, if so, whether it produces gas.

Investigation #4   Microscopic survey of bacteria

In the following exercises you will examine several slides. You will use the oil immersion lens for the first time. Be sure to clean the oil from the microscope and the slides with lens paper when you are done.

1. Obtain a prepared slide of mixed bacterial types. This slide has bacteria representing the three shapes of bacteria: bacilli, cocci, and spirilla. Under low power, find a portion of the slide that contains a diverse collection of cell types. Examine under high power. Try to center a group that shows all three shapes.
2. Next, raise the nosepiece so that the objectives are well clear of the slide. Switch to the oil immersion lens. Place a small drop of oil on the center of the slide. Now, watching from the side of the microscope, carefully lower the objective so that it makes contact with the oil. You should be able to focus the image with the fine adjustment knob. If necessary, adjust the diaphragm to let in more light.
3. Next, obtain a prepared slide of clover root nodules. Focus on a nodule and work up to oil immersion. Can you see the symbiotic bacteria? Where are they relative to the root cells?

Investigation #5   Preparing and staining smears

Now you will make your own slides. You will make **smears** by spreading the cells onto the slide in a thin suspension. After the smears are **heat fixed** to the slide, they can be stained. The specimens you prepare will be examples of particular arrangements of cell growth. Since the individual cells of a string or cluster can be mechanically broken apart, it is best to culture the bacteria in broth rather than on agar for such study; it is difficult to preserve these cell groupings when they are scraped off of agar to make a slide.

The instructions below are general directions for any stained smear. You will follow them twice to make separate slides from cultures of *Enterococcus faecalis* and *Staphylococcus epidermidis*.

1. On the bottom of a clean slide, draw a circle about the size of a dime. This will be your guide.
2. Using aseptic technique, transfer 2-3 loopfuls of bacteria to the center of the circle. Flame your loop between loopfuls. Spread the culture around within the circle. Flame your loop.

3. Let the slides air dry. Blowing or heating the slide at this stage will distort the specimen. If you spread your suspension thin enough, this will not take long.
4. When the slide is <u>completely</u> dry, heat fix it by passing it through a flame 2 or 3 times.
5. Hold the slide with a clothespin while you stain it. Cover the smear with methylene blue and leave it for 60 seconds.
6. Hold the slide at an angle over a sink or staining tray and rinse excess stain from the slide with a gentle stream of distilled water from a wash bottle. Gently blot the slide with a paper towel and let it air dry.
7. A stained smear does not need a cover slip when it is dry. Oil can be placed directly on the smear.
8. You may also make smears of unknowns from your environmental plate. Since these are not in broth medium, put a small drop of water on your slide first. Then take up a bit of bacteria with a sterile loop and smear it in the water drop. At that point you can let the slide air dry for heat fixing as in step 3 above.

Important Terms

agar
aerobe
aerotolerant
anaerobe
Archaea
aseptic technique
autoclave
autotroph
bacillus
Bacteria
broth
coccus
colony
commensalism
culture
domain
Eukarya
exoenzyme
facultative anaerobe
halophile
heat fixing
heterotroph
inoculating loop
medium
methanogen
mutualism
nitrogen fixation
nodule
nutrient agar
nutrient broth
obligate anaerobe
parasite
parasitism
pasteurization
phototroph
plate
saprotroph
smear
spirillum
spirochete
staphylococcus
streptococcus
symbiosis
thermophile

CHAPTER 6
THE DOMAINS OF LIFE
PART II: EUKARYA

INTRODUCTION

The most ancient fossils of eukaryotic cells yet discovered are only about 2 billion years old – considerably younger than prokaryotes, which go back at least 3.5 billion years. As discussed in the previous chapter, it is currently believed that eukaryotes evolved from some ancient relative of thermoacidophile archaea. Exactly how the nucleus and cytoskeleton arose is not very clear. However, virtually all eukaryotic cells possess mitochondria, and what we have learned about their origin is rather strange.

   Mitochondria are at the center of an evolutionary question which biologists began to debate in the 1920's. Mitochondria (and chloroplasts, which will be taken up in the next chapter) seem very similar to certain bacteria. They are about the same size and, critically, contain circular chromosomes independent of the eukaryotic chromosomes in the nucleus. This led some biologists to speculate that mitochondria arose when some bacteria started living inside of larger cells and eventually became dependent on their hosts. That is, mitochondria were thought to be derived from bacteria that lived symbiotically inside of other cells, not unlike the nitrogen-fixing bacteria of root cells discussed in the previous chapter. Since this theory postulated that mitochondria originated with one species living <u>inside</u> another's cells, it was called the **endosymbiotic** theory (from the Greek *endon*, within). The endosymbiotic theory did not explain everything about how eukaryotes first came about (for example, it said nothing about nuclei or why eukaryotic chromosomes are so much larger and more complex than prokaryotic chromosomes) but for various reasons it became popular among microbiologists during the 1970's. Unfortunately, it was almost impossible to test experimentally.

Figure 6.1.   Endosymbiotic origin of mitochondria

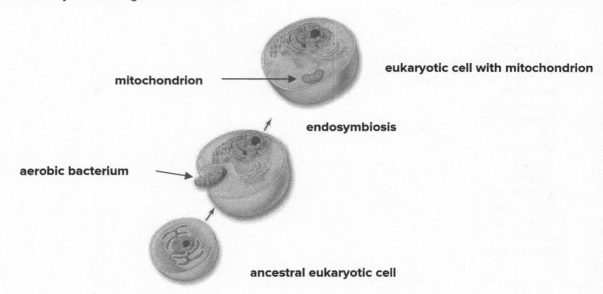

Once Carl Woese discovered that there were two kinds of prokaryotes, biologists decided to see if mitochondria and chloroplasts were homologous with either kind. As you know, the genes in the nucleus were determined to be related to those of archaea. A big surprise came when it was found that the DNA in mitochondria and chloroplasts is homologous to that of different groups of bacteria! This essentially proved the endosymbiotic theory, for the only way one part of the cell could have evolved from one domain and the rest from a different domain was for the different parts to have come together after millions of years of being separate. In a way, eukaryotes are in not actually a separate domain, but a mixture of the other two. Many mitochondrial and chloroplast genes can be traced back to bacterial ancestors, while many nuclear genes can be traced back to their archaeal roots. We have noted that many archaea live in oxygen-poor environments, so it may be that they acquired aerobic bacteria as endosymbionts (that is, as mitochondria) in order to deal with levels of oxygen that began to rise about 2.5 billion years ago.

Since there are no known multicellular bacteria, it seems safe to assume that the first eukaryotes were unicellular. Today there are many species of unicellular eukaryotes. They are all grouped together (along with a few kinds of multicellular organisms) under the term **protists**.

The protists are a tangled collection of the most ancient lines of eukaryotic evolution. They do not constitute a true phylogenetic kingdom so much as a grouping of many different creatures that do not really fit in any of the other kingdoms. In practical terms, this means that the various protist divisions and phyla are studied by many different specialists. Some seem animal-like because they are mobile and heterotrophic – these are referred to as **protozoa** (from the Greek words *protos*, first, and *zoon*, animal; note the subtle difference between the word "protozoa" and the more inclusive term "protist!") and are studied by protozoologists and zoologists. Photosynthetic protists are called **algae** and are studied by algologists and botanists. A few protists are reminiscent of fungi and are usually studied by mycologists and botanists; they have no collective name but are grouped together as "fungal protists." In this chapter we will consider a few types of protozoa and one kind of fungal protist. We will look at algae in the next chapter.

MITOSIS, MEIOSIS, AND SEXUAL REPRODUCTION

The defining characteristic of all eukaryotes is the nucleus, which contains the bulk of the cell's DNA, arranged in long ribbonlike chromosomes. Bacteria have chromosomes too, but they are small and circular instead of straight. Moreover, a bacterium has only a single chromosome (although some species may have tiny secondary chromosomes called plasmids) while eukaryotes can have anywhere from a few to hundreds of chromosomes – each species has its own particular number.

When any cell divides, its DNA first replicates itself so that each new cell will have its own copy. In bacteria this process is relatively simple. In eukaryotes, each separate chromosome must replicate and then they must be sorted into two complete sets. This is accomplished by the process of mitosis. Most kinds of eukaryotes are also able to combine sets of chromosomes in sexual reproduction. At some point prior to sexual reproduction cells must undergo the process of meiosis so that each sex cell has only half of each pair of chromosomes. A nucleus with both chromosomes from each pair (as in most of the cells in your body) is diploid, and nuclei with only half of each pair (as in sperm and eggs) are haploid.

For many unicellular protists, the average cell is haploid. These can divide mitotically to produce more haploid individuals. Cells formed by mitosis are always identical unless a mutation occurs. Occasionally two haploid individuals will fuse to form a zygote, which then divides meiotically to form new haploid individuals. This process reshuffles the chromosome pairs and introduces genetic diversity without mutations. For species in which the average cell is diploid, meiosis occurs before two cells can fuse. Most protists reproduce both asexually and sexually. We will look at this in more detail in the ciliates and slime molds.

PROTIST WAYS OF MOVING

Another key characteristic of eukaryotic cells is the cytoskeleton. The cytoskeleton shapes and organizes the cell. However, it is not rigid like an animal skeleton. Rather, the elements of the cytoskeleton can slide along each other to make the cell stretch, change shape, and move. For example, muscle cells have a highly specialized cytoskeleton, which is what allows them to contract.

The cytoskeleton of protists is usually modified in some way to permit movement. One possibility is called **amoeboid movement**. This is used by flexible cells that constantly change their shapes. They pull themselves along submerged materials using temporary extensions of their bodies called **pseudopodia**. Two other forms of movement involve thin, hair-like projections of the cytoskeleton. Long **flagella** rotate like propellers, although they are often described as "tails." Cells can have one or multiple flagella, and they can be at the back of the cell to push it or at the front to pull it. **Cilia** are structurally very similar to flagella but are shorter and move back and forth like oars rather than rotating. Ciliated cells always have many cilia. In the following exercises you will see examples of protozoa that use each of these methods of movement. It is important to remember that they are all variations on the same cytoskeletal system. Indeed, in some species cells can even change from amoeboid to flagellated. The human body contains cells of all three types.

REPRESENTATIVE PROTOZOAN PHYLA

There are many phyla of protozoa, but all are mobile unicellular heterotrophs. Protozoa do not have cell walls, which makes their bodies more or less flexible. Many species are able to draw smaller organisms (bacteria or smaller protists) through their cell membranes as food. Other species are parasites, obtaining predigested food from their hosts. Like all protists, protozoa are limited to moist habitats. Most are aquatic, but some live in moist soil or inside of other organisms as symbionts. Although grouped together as "protozoa," the evolutionary relationships between these phyla are far from clear.

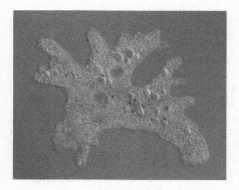

Figure 6.2. Amoeba
Getty Images/iStockphoto

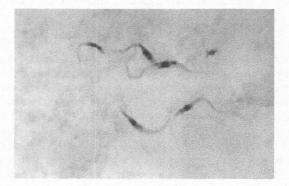

Figure 6.3. Trypanosome
Courtesy of the CDC

AMOEBAS

There are actually several different phyla of **amoebas**; perhaps the most prominent is Phylum Gymnamoeba. Amoebas (figure 6.2) are predatory, and use their pseudopodia to engulf prey. When the prey is completely surrounded by the pseudopod, the part of the cell membrane which was drawn in with the prey pinches off and moves around inside the amoeba like a food-filled bubble. Such bubbles are called food **vacuoles**, and the process of engulfing prey is called **phagocytosis**. Amoebas and other protists also contain specialized **contractile vacuoles** which pump excess water out of the organism (similar to a human kidney).

Amoeboid cells appear to have arisen many different times in evolutionary history, and the term **amoeboid** has come to describe any kind of shapeless, phagocytic cell. Amoebas are popularly thought of as the "simplest" or "lowest" form of life, but this idea does not do justice to their ability to perform all of the functions necessary for life in but a single cell. Nevertheless, sexual reproduction has never been observed in most amoebas.

FLAGELLATES

Many protists move via flagella. Phylum Kinetoplastida is distinguished from other types of **flagellates** by an unusual mitochondrion that contains a structure called a kinetoplast, but that detail will not concern us here. Many **kinetoplastids** are predatory but several are important parasites. For example, different species of trypanosomes (figure 6.3) cause a variety of tropical diseases, including African sleeping sickness and Chagas disease. They live in blood.

CILIATES

Ciliates are grouped in Phylum Ciliophora. They are very elaborate structurally — as active predators they are well-adapted to seek out and capture prey. All ciliates possess cilia; some are covered with them while others have bands of cilia on particular regions of their bodies. The cilia can propel the ciliates at relatively high speeds. Ciliates are not phagocytic like amoebas. Instead they have an invagination of their cell membranes called an **oral groove**. Prey are swept into the oral groove by the beating action of the cilia. When the food particles contact a specialized area at the back of the oral groove, they are surrounded by the membrane and drawn into the cell as a food vacuole. Some ciliates also have defensive structures called trichocysts — fibrous darts that are discharged when the cell is disturbed.

Figure 6.4. *Paramecium*

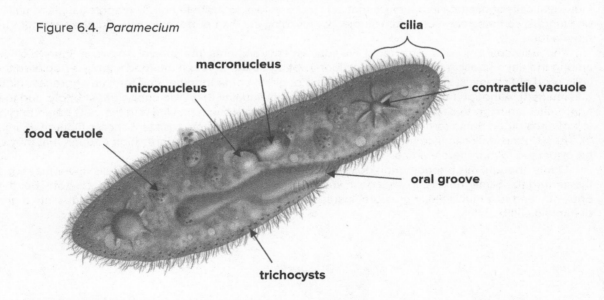

Most ciliates contain two types of nuclei: the **micronucleus** and the **macronucleus**. The macronucleus controls the cell but the micronuclei can undergo meiosis and participate in sexual **conjugation**. When ciliates of opposite mating types (they do not have distinct sexes) conjugate, their macronuclei dissolve. Each gives the other cell a haploid micronucleus to fuse with one of its own haploid micronuclei. The resulting diploid micronucleus then gives rise to a genetically new macronucleus. After conjugation, the two cells separate. Thus, in ciliates, sex is separate from reproduction – two cells enter the process and two remain at the end. Conjugation allows the cells to alter their own genetic identity. Ciliates reproduce by a simple form of cell division called **fission**.

Figure 6.5. Conjugating paramecia exchanging micronuclei

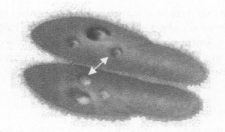

CELLULAR SLIME MOLDS

Cellular slime molds (Division Dictyostelida[*]) bridge the gap between single-celled and multicellular organisms. Most of their lives are spent as independent amoeboid cells, but when they run out of food the individual cells aggregate into a mass that acts more or less as a single unit. The aggregate is reminiscent of a fungus, so these are more often studied by mycologists than protozoologists. But they are not true fungi either.

The individual cells of a slime mold live in moist environments (the species shown in figure 6.6 lives among the decomposing leaves on forest floors) eating bacteria. When the food supply is depleted the cells send out chemical signals to each other and begin to come together and form an aggregate (figure 6.6, image 1). Although the cells retain much of their individuality they also cooperate strongly, and the aggregate can migrate as a unit. At some point the aggregate stops moving and the cells begin to climb on top of each other. Some form a stalk, and those at the top change into resistant spores (figure 6.6, image 6). Those in the stalk sacrifice themselves in order to raise the head of spores high enough that they can be dispersed to more fertile areas.

Oddly enough, this phenomenon does not involve sexual reproduction – the cells never fuse within the aggregate. Slime molds can engage in sex when two individual cells fuse to form a zygote. But this does not lead to a multicellular creature. Instead, the zygote undergoes meiosis and divides into a group of haploid cells.

---

[*] Recall that the term "division" is used instead of "phylum" for plants and groups once considered plants (algae, bacteria, fungi).

Figure 6.6. Life stages *Dictyostelium*

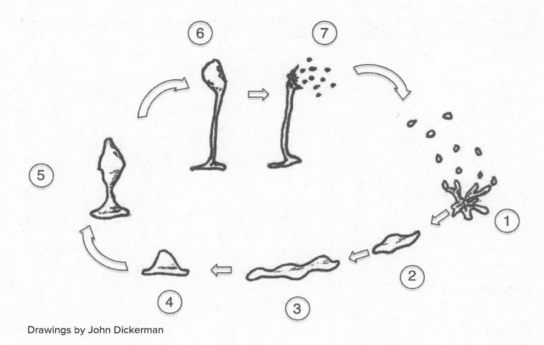

Drawings by John Dickerman

INVESTIGATIONS WITH PROTISTS

In the following exercises you will examine both living and preserved protists. Try to identify as many structures as you can from the diagrams.

Investigation #1   Survey of protozoa
When looking at the living protozoa, pay attention to their method of movement. Fast-swimming creatures can be slowed down by adding a drop of viscous methyl cellulose solution to the slide. The best way to view living protists is under phase contrast.

1.   **Amoebas**: Make a wet mount from the mixture of live amoeboid species. These will vary in size. Remember that amoebas crawl along the surfaces of objects, so they will tend to be at the bottom of the culture jar. Observe their structure under the microscope and compare what you see with figure 6.2. Observe the motion of the pseudopodia.
2.   **Flagellates**: Examine a prepared slide of *Trypanosoma*. Note the general appearance and the position of the flagella.

Investigation #2   Characteristics of Ciliates
Ciliates are also protozoa, but they are very complex.

1.   **Survey of Ciliates**: There are many common genera of ciliates. We will have a mixture of living specimens to examine. Ciliates can vary by size and shape. Some are even colored (e.g., *Stentor* is blue and *Blepharisma* is pink). Examine the specimens for arrangement of cilia and the position of the oral groove. Look for the other structures in figure 6.4.
2.   **Predation in the Ciliates**: Examine a prepared slide of *Didinium*. *Didinium* is a voracious predator that often eats other ciliates. Look for cells that are ingesting other cells.
3.   **Reproduction in the Ciliates**: Compare prepared slides of *Paramecium* conjugation and division (fission). Be sure you can recognize each process. Which one is reproduction?

Investigation #3 *Dictyostelium* **life cycle**

Dictyostelium is the best known genus of slime molds. It is often used in experiments on how cells communicate and cooperate.

1.   **Aggregation:** Observe a culture plate of living *Dictyostelium* under a dissecting microscope. Can you find aggregates? Do they have spore stalks?

Important Terms

algae
amoeba
amoeboid
amoeboid movement
cilia
ciliate
conjugation
contractile vacuole
endosymbiosis
endosymbiotic theory
fission
flagellate
flagellum
kinetoplastid
macronucleus
micronucleus
oral groove
phagocytosis
protist
protozoa
pseudopod
vacuole

CHAPTER 7
ALGAE:
PHOTOSYNTHESIS AND THE ORIGINS
OF MULTICELLULARITY

INTRODUCTION

All organisms require energy to live. We have seen that heterotrophs obtain energy when they ingest energy-rich compounds like carbohydrates. It is thought that the early earth probably had organic materials in the environment that heterotrophs could use for food, but these materials would eventually run out as life multiplied. On the other hand, autotrophs make their own organic compounds using CO_2 from the environment using some other external energy source. Some autotrophic prokaryotes get their energy from inorganic minerals. These organisms are critical to the ecology of deep sea hydrothermal vent communities, and were probably important on the early earth. But eventually some cells evolved the ability to tap a greater energy source: the sun.

BACTERIAL PHOTOSYNTHESIS

Phototrophs employ the process of photosynthesis to convert light energy into chemical energy. It is this chemical energy which is then used to build organic molecules out of carbon dioxide. Since heterotrophs get their energy from these same organic compounds, they too rely on photosynthesis as their ultimate energy source, albeit indirectly. The process of photosynthesis is thus of crucial importance to the entire living world.

All eukaryotes use essentially the same kind of photosynthesis, in which light energy is used to turn water and carbon dioxide into carbohydrate and oxygen:

$$6\ H_2O\ +\ 6\ CO_2\ \text{-->}\ C_6H_{12}O_6\ +\ 6\ O_2$$

The various eukaryotes differ mainly in what kind of pigment molecules they use to absorb and trap light.

The oxygen produced by photosynthesis is the same oxygen used by aerobic organisms to burn carbohydrates back into water and carbon dioxide. However, not all bacteria produce oxygen when they photosynthesize. In the billions of years that they have been on earth, bacteria have developed several varieties of photosynthesis, and some of the most primitive systems give off sulfur instead of oxygen. Indeed, the **purple** and **green sulfur bacteria** are obligate anaerobes, unable to grow in the presence of oxygen. Those photosynthetic bacteria that do produce oxygen still vary greatly in which pigments they contain and can be almost any color: red, brown, green, and blue-green species are all common.

Some species can photosynthesize under some conditions but live heterotrophically in others. For example, a bacterium called *Rhodopseudomonas spheroides* is a pale heterotroph when cultured aerobically on nutrient agar. However, in the absence of oxygen it can still grow if exposed to light. In an anaerobic environment *Rhodopseudomonas* produces brilliant red photosynthetic pigments and looks like a totally different species.

CYANOBACTERIA

When iron is exposed to oxygen, it rusts. Because our atmosphere is about 21% oxygen, there is very little pure iron on the surface of the earth — most rusted into various kinds of ores long ago. However, locked inside of very old rocks are bits of unoxidized iron. This indicates that at one time (over two and a half billion years ago) the earth's atmosphere contained very little oxygen. How did the atmosphere change as it did? The fossil record suggests that it was due to the appearance of a certain kind of photosynthetic bacteria called **cyanobacteria**. These were among the first bacteria to give off oxygen as a by-product of photosynthesis, and they were so successful and abundant that they completely changed the composition of the air and forced the living world to be dominated by aerobes.

Cyanobacteria are still fairly common and ecologically important. They are eaten by many aquatic organisms and so are an important source of energy and organic compounds in these aquatic communities. Some species are also able to fix nitrogen. Cyanobacteria are not as powerful at nitrogen-fixation as the bacteria that live in root nodules. However, those cyanobacteria that are both nitrogen-fixers and autotrophs are the most self-sufficient kind of life on earth.

Figure 7.1.   The cyanobacterium *Anabaena*, showing heterocysts specialized for nitrogen-fixation

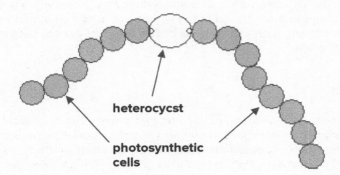

heterocycst

photosynthetic cells

The oxygen-producing reactions cyanobacteria use in photosynthesis are essentially the same as those used by photosynthetic eukaryotes. However, some of the pigments that cyanobacteria use to absorb light are unusual. These pigments, called **phycobilins**, often give the cyanobacteria a blue-green color, which accounts for the common name of cyanobacteria: **blue-green algae**. However, it must be stressed that not all species of cyanobacteria are blue-green: they can be almost any color and many species are red. In fact, the only other major group of phototrophs that contains phycobillin pigments is the red algae.

CHLOROPLASTS AND ENDOSYMBIOSIS

In chapter 6 we pointed out that eukaryotic cells arose as fusions of two unrelated types of cells: bacterial symbionts inside of archaeal hosts. The original endosymbiotic event led to mitochondria. The vast majority of eukaryotic cells have mitochondria, and the few that do not have various structures that suggest that their ancestors had mitochondria too. Indeed, the DNA still found inside mitochondria indicate that they all came from a single common ancestor, and that DNA can be used fairly successfully to reconstruct eukaryotic phylogeny.

On the other hand, chloroplasts have a rather different history. Only algae and plants have them, and the chloroplasts of these different groups vary considerably. So it appears that after the original eukaryote formed from a thermophilic archaeon that had developed a nucleus and taken in a mitochondrion, there were several independent events that led to different groups obtaining chloroplasts. This is not as odd as it may at first seem: in the coming chapters you will even see examples of fungi and animals that have algae growing inside of their tissues. In the cases of the fungi and animals, the algae can be extracted and cultured separately, as they do not absolutely depend upon their hosts to survive. However, if, over time, the algae lost their independence, we would see the origins of new kinds of chloroplasts.

Gene sequences and physiology indicate that all chloroplasts are descended ultimately from cyanobacteria; they all use similar photosystems and enzymes to perform the Hill reaction and Calvin cycle. But the paths some of these chloroplasts have taken are not simple. The chloroplasts of some algae contain extra membranes and occasionally even vestigial nuclei – these chloroplasts seem to have arisen from endosymbiotic <u>eukaryotic</u> algae. That is, the chloroplasts of some species are endosymbionts within endosymbionts. This process is called **secondary endosymbiosis**.

Figure 7.2.   Chloroplasts originating via endosymbiosis and secondary endosymbiosis

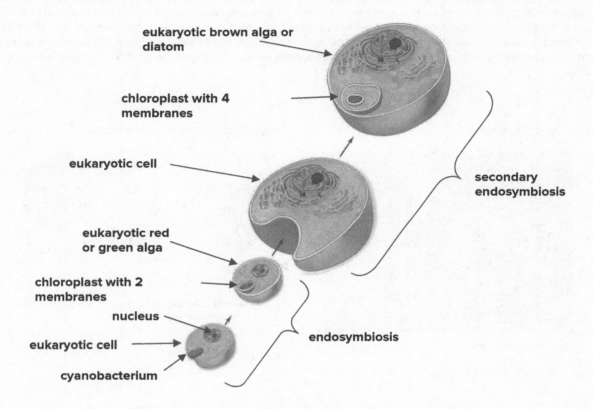

REPRESENTATIVE ALGAL DIVISIONS

The first eukaryotes with chloroplasts were algae. Algae are aquatic organisms, living in either fresh water or sea water; a few can live in moist terrestrial environments. The modification of some algae to live on dry land led to the origin of plants.

The algae are a diverse group of protists, representing several divergent lines of evolution which are only distantly related. Many species of algae are unicellular, but quite a few are multicellular and macroscopic. Some species of brown algae can even grow to enormous sizes.

Because they are photosynthetic, the algae are ecologically very important – they feed most of the creatures of the world's seas, rivers, and lakes. We will look at five divisions in this chapter. Characteristics used to classify algae include: overall morphology, types of chlorophyll present, types of accessory photosynthetic pigments present, kinds of carbohydrate produced, and cell wall structure and composition. We will only consider some of these traits for any particular group. All of the groups listed below are capable of sexual reproduction, either by fusion of unicellular individuals or through the union of sperm and eggs produced by multicellular individuals. We will not consider the details of any algal life cycles. Most of the division names of the algae end in *-phyta*, from the Greek word for plant, *phyton*.

UNICELLULAR ALGAE

Two widespread groups of unicellular algae are the **diatoms** (Division Bacillariophyta) and the **dinoflagellates** (Division Dinoflagellata). In many aquatic ecosystems these creatures are important producers at the base of the food chain.

Diatoms are best known for their unique cell walls made of **silica**, the same material found in glass (see figure 7.3). Each diatom cell wall has two halves which fit together like the parts of a petri dish. Because of their glassy composition and grooved structure they tend to have a faceted, prismatic appearance. The cell walls of dead diatoms form a gritty material called **diatomaceous earth** which has many economic uses: as a fine abrasive material, as a reflective glitter for paints, or as a filtration medium. It is even used as an insecticide (insects eat it and the tiny grains of glass injure their digestive tracts). Diatom chloroplasts contain chlorophylls *a* and *c*; concentrated **carotenoid** accessory pigments give them a golden-brown color.

Figure 7.3. Diatoms

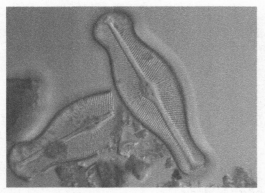

Sarah Spaulding/USGS

Figure 7.4. Some dinoflagellates

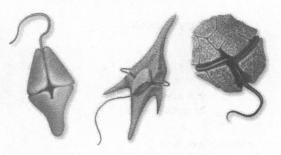

Dinoflagellates also contain chlorophylls *a* and *c* and carotenoids. As a result they range in color from red to brown. These are the organisms responsible for "**red tides**," huge algae blooms that can turn vast stretches of water red in color. Since some dinoflagellates produce toxic compounds, red tides usually cause fish kills and can make seafood inedible. They can also be a significant health hazard to humans. Red tides are becoming more common due to fertilizers polluting streams and rivers, and are now a major environmental concern.

Dinoflagellates possess a pair of flagella, of which one is located in a groove around the middle of the organism (figure 7.4). Many species are surrounded by an unusual cell wall made of cellulose plates. **Cellulose** is the carbohydrate that also makes up wood and other plant fibers.

GREEN ALGAE

Green algae (Division Chlorophyta) are incredibly diverse. Freshwater or marine, they can range from unicellular to multicellular and come in all shapes and sizes. This diversity suggests that green algae are an ancient group that has had a great deal of time to adapt to many environments and ways of life.

The range of sizes in green algae tells us something about how multicellularity evolved. In between the unicellular species and the larger multicellular species are many **colonial** species. Colonial protists live as small masses of interconnected cells (i.e., colonies), similar to multicellular organisms. But unlike true multicellular organisms, if the cells of a colony are broken apart the organism does not die; each separate cell divides on its own to form a new colony. And even though the cells of the colony are interconnected, they are not differentiated into specialized tissues. On the other hand, a colonial species generally seeks to maintain itself in the colonial state, so it is more organized than the temporary aggregations made by cellular slime molds.

Green algal chloroplasts are relatively simple, resembling their cyanobacterial ancestors except that they contain two types of chlorophyll (chlorophylls *a* and *b*) and lack phycobilins. They contain small amounts of carotenoids. Green algae store carbohydrates as starch and make their cell walls out of cellulose. In this they greatly resemble land plants and are considered ancestral to plants.

Like most protists, the greens are capable of sexual reproduction. In the simpler types this is often by a form of conjugation. Unlike ciliate conjugation, however, conjugation in green algae is not limited to the exchange of micronuclei, but involves the fusion of two haploid cells. This is accomplished by fusing the cell walls of male and female cells so that the male cell can crawl inside the cell wall of the female and join with it. The zygote, or fertilized egg, develops inside the old cell wall of the egg cell.

MACROSCOPIC ALGAE

Two divisions of algae are dominated by relatively large species: **brown algae** (Division Phaeophyta) and **red algae** (Division Rhodophyta). All brown algae are multicellular, and while some species of red algae are unicellular, they are not typical. These groups are essentially marine; only a few species of red algae (and no known species of brown algae) live in fresh water. People in coastal areas use both types for food.

Red algae are unusual in many ways. They produce several peculiar carbohydrates, including **agar**, which we use in the laboratory to solidify bacterial media, and **carrageenan**, which is often used to thicken foods like ice cream. Their chloroplasts are very similar to cyanobacteria and contain chlorophyll *a* (but not chlorophyll *b* or *c*) and the accessory pigment phycoerythrin, a protein complexed to phycobilin pigments. Thus they are usually red in color but can also be blue or even black. The pigments found in red algae are apparently very good at scavenging energy from dim light, as these organisms are frequently found deeper in coastal waters than other algae.

Ranging in length from 3 inches to 300 feet, the brown algae include the largest and most complex species of algae. Their chloroplasts contain chlorophylls *a* and *c* and various carotenoids, which give them their color. The most elaborate species are commonly called "**kelps**." These are anchored to submerged surfaces by a structure called a **holdfast** (figure 7.5) which is analogous to the roots of a plant. A long **stipe**, analogous to a stem, reaches to the surface where leafy **blades** are exposed to the light. The blades sometimes have air bladders to help them float. Despite their size and complexity, brown algae are not related to land plants.

Figure 7.5. Kelp morphology

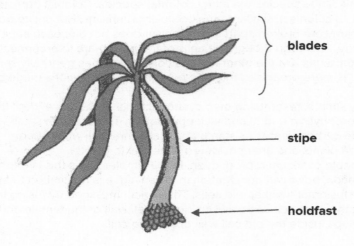

blades

stipe

holdfast

INVESTIGATIONS WITH CYANOBACTERIA AND ALGAE

Investigation #1   Survey of photosynthetic bacteria cyanobacteria
The only way to tell if an unknown bacterium is photosynthetic or not is to see if it will grow in a carbon-poor medium when exposed to light. However, one rule you can remember is that <u>a photosynthetic organism must be colored</u> – pigments are necessary for collecting light energy. (The converse of this is not always true, however – some heterotrophic organisms are also pigmented.) Cyanobacteria can be distinguished from other photosynthetic bacteria in that they are always aerobic and are often relatively large for bacteria. They differ from the true algae because they are prokaryotic, which is obvious under a microscope since their pigments are distributed throughout their cells instead of being localized in chloroplasts.
1.   Depending on availability, several types of photosynthetic bacteria besides cyanobacteria may be on display. Observe the different types of bacterial colonies. Note the colors of each. Note their mode of oxygen utilization: aerobic, facultative, or obligately anaerobic.
2.   Cyanobacteria can form strings or clusters like other bacteria, but terms like "streptococcus" are rarely applied to them. Strings of cyanobacteria are described as **filamentous**, a term also used with eukaryotic algae. Look for heterocysts in the filamentous *Anabaena*. These are specialized cells where nitrogen fixation occurs.

Investigation #2   Survey of unicellular algae
Unicellular algae must be examined microscopically like protozoa but their photosynthetic pigments make them easier to see.
1.   **Diatoms**: Examine a prepared slide of diatoms. All you are actually seeing are the leftover frustules of dead diatoms – note how they refract light like cut glass.
2.   **Dinoflagellates**: View a slide of mixed dinoflagellates. Compare them to figure 7.4. See if you can locate the flagellum and groove around the middle of each cell.

Investigation #3   Survey of green algae
Green algae can range from microscopic unicells to large seaweeds. Larger specimens are stored in jars in preservative solution or are dried onto paper as herbarium sheets. The process of preservation may cause specimens to fade or become completely colorless, but all photosynthetic algae are pigmented in life.

1. **Volvocine algae:** One interesting group of green algae contains many living species that can be lined up in a continuum of increasing complexity, presumably mirroring the evolutionary history of the group. Make a wet mount slide from the living culture of "mixed Volvocales." The simplest species in the mix is unicellular. Each cell has two flagella, so they are mobile. There are also colonial species of various sizes, but each cell of the colonies resemble the individuals of the unicellular species. The largest colonies belong to *Volvox*. Each *Volvox* colony is actually a hollow sphere with all of its cells on the surface. Inside the lumen of the colony may be daughter colonies which will live independently when the parent colony dies and breaks apart. In *Volvox* specialized cells engage in reproduction. Sometimes these cells give rise directly to the daughter colonies asexually, and sometimes they produce sperm and eggs for sexual reproduction. Look for daughter colonies. Fertilized zygotes are orange.
2. **Multicellular green algae:** Preserved and dried specimens of several species will be on display. Note the range of body types.

Investigation #4 Survey of macroscopic algae
1. **Rhodophyta:** Observe the delicate filamentous form of *Polysiphonia* as preserved on herbarium sheets. Note the range of body types displayed on the herbarium sheets of genera such as *Chondrus*, *Gigaretina*, and *Smithora*.
2. **Phaeophyta:** *Ectocarpus* is a relatively small filamentous brown alga. Examine the morphology of preserved specimens on herbarium sheets. Larger kelps, such as *Fucus* and *Ascophyllum* (from the North Atlantic coast) and *Postelsia* and *Macrocystis* (from the Pacific coast) are displayed on herbarium sheets and in preservative solution.

Investigation #5 Chloroplast diversity and origins
The pigments in chloroplasts can be extracted, separated by chromatography, and analyzed by spectrophotometry. Scientists have done this for many types of algae and bacteria, and the results for a few are summarized in the table below. The table also indicates how many membranes bound the chloroplasts, as indicated by electron microscopy.

Organism	chlorophylls	membranes	accessory pigments
cyanobacteria	*a*	1	carotenoids & phycobilins
brown algae	*a* & *c*	4	carotenoids
diatoms	*a* & *c*	4	carotenoids
dinoflagellates	*a* & *c*	4	carotenoids
green algae	*a* & *b*	2	carotenoids
red algae	*a*	2	carotenoids & phycobilins

(Carotenoids are actually a whole class of pigments that can be separated into individual compounds – such as carotene and xanthophyll – by chromatography. The same is true of phycobilins. We will not concern ourselves with these details here. Instead we will treat each class as a single pigment.)
1. Divide the organisms in the table into groups having similar pigments. Where does the prokaryote fit best? What modifications does it need to fall in with the other types of algae?
2. Construct a simple tree showing how an ancestral eukaryotic line could have branched into the groups identified in step one. Does each branch suggests a separate endosymbiotic origin for the chloroplasts in that group? Do any of the branches then sub-divide after the chloroplasts are acquired? What is the minimum number of endosymbiotic events necessary to account for these data? Can you tell if history might have entailed more than this minimum number?

Important Terms

agar
blade
blue-green algae
brown algae
carotenoid
carrageenan
cellulose
colonial
cyanobacteria
diatom
diatomaceous earth
dinoflagellate
filamentous
green algae
green sulfur bacteria
holdfast
kelp
phycobilin
purple sulfur bacteria
red algae
red tide
secondary endosymbiosis
silica
stipe

Summary of Protist Characteristics (Chapters 6 & 7)

phylum/division	body	mobility	sexual	cell wall material	chlorophyll	pigments
Bacillariophyta	unicellular	special	yes	silica	*a & c*	carotenoid
Chlorophyta	uni- to multicellular	flagella	yes	cellulose	*a & b*	carotenoid
Ciliophora	unicellular	cilia	conjugation	no	no	no
Dictyostelida	aggregate	pseudopodia	yes	no	no	no
Dinoflagellata	unicellular	flagella	rare	cellulose	*a & c*	carotenoid
Gymnamoeba	unicellular	pseudopodia	no	no	no	no
Kinetoplastida	unicellular	flagella	rare	no	no	no
Phaeophyta	multicellular	*	yes	cellulose, algin	*a & c*	carotenoid
Rhodophyta	multicellular	no	yes	cellulose, agar, carrageenin	*a*	phycobilins

* Only certain reproductive cells

CHAPTER 8
FUNGI

INTRODUCTION

Like algae, fungi were once generally regarded as a type of "primitive plant." However, aside from living in moist soil, fungi have almost nothing in common with plants. They are not photosynthetic and DNA sequences indicate that they are more closely related to animals than they are to anything else, even though they are quite different in overall appearance.

Fungi are large saprotrophs with strange filamentous bodies called **mycelia**. A mycelium is a mass of threads called **hyphae**. Instead of cellulose, the cell walls of fungi are made of the unusual carbohydrate **chitin**, a polymer of glucosamine. No other groups of organisms have chitinous cell walls, although many animals use chitin to strengthen some of their tissues. Fungi are unable to ingest food particles because of their cell walls and live as either saprotrophs or parasites. Some saprotrophic fungi are able to digest substances that even bacteria cannot metabolize, and therefore play a vital role in the world's ecology by recycling nutrients that would otherwise be locked up in the bodies of dead organisms and other biological waste.

Although people seldom think about them, fungi are extremely important economically. Parasitic fungi cause many diseases in crops and animals while saprotrophic fungi are responsible for decaying vast amounts of food, lumber, and textiles. On the other hand fungi produce many exoenzymes which are industrially useful (for example, the enzymes used to convert corn starch into corn syrup). Some also make other important compounds such as antibiotics. Yeast, a type of unicellular fungus, is critical to baking and making alcohol because of its ability to ferment inside of foods. For these reasons food and drug companies culture tons of various fungi every year.

Fungi are poorly represented in the fossil record, but mycelial organisms appear to be among the earliest eukaryotes. Fungi have traditionally been classified on the basis of what kind of reproductive structures and spores they produce. Molecular homologies are now being used to clarify relationships among the various types of fungi.

Figure 8.1.   Life cycle of *Rhizopus*, a zygomycete

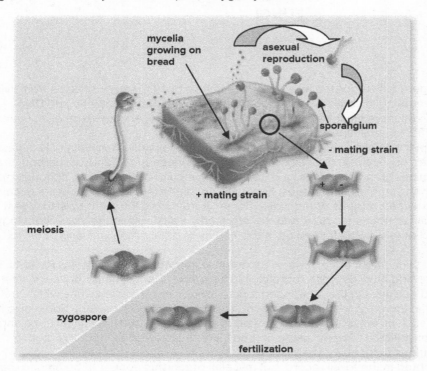

REPRESENTATIVE DIVISIONS OF FUNGI

There are at least four major divisions of fungi. Most are defined by particular methods of sexual reproduction and spore production, and the formal names of these fungal divisions are composed of the names of their distinctive sexual spores combined with the ending -*mycota* (from the Greek word for mushroom, *mykes*). We will describe two such divisions and then look at how certain fungi participate in important mutualistic symbioses.

Zygomycetes (Division Zygomycota) are a relatively simple type of fungus best known for spoiling foods like bread. There are about 1,000 species of zygomycetes but they are difficult to tell apart.

Like many fungi, zygomycetes can reproduce in two different ways — asexually and sexually. A single mycelium can produce raised **sporangia** full of haploid spores via mitosis. These spores germinate into haploid mycelia genetically identical to the parent.

Two different mycelia may also grow together and engage in sexual reproduction. The "difference" between the mycelia cannot be seen, but for any given species there are "plus" and "minus" mating strains that function like sexes except that they are structurally identical. Opposite strains are able to fuse by **conjugation** (conjugation is a generic term derived from a Latin word meaning "to couple" — zygomycete conjugation is not the same as ciliate conjugation). This forms one or more diploid zygotes which become encased in a round object called a **zygospore**. The zygotes exist only within the dormant zygospore. Meiosis occurs inside the zygospore prior to germination so that the new mycelium will be haploid like the parents. Both sporangia and zygospores are illustrated in figure 8.1.

Basidiomycetes (Division Basidiomycota) include the most familiar fungi. The basidiomycetes are a diverse group and include many plant pathogens such as corn smut and wheat rust. Common mushrooms and puffballs are also basidiomycetes. Actually, the mushrooms and puffballs that you see are masses of hyphae compressed into reproductive structures called **basidiocarps** — the body of the basidiomycete is a mycelium, usually hidden underground or in a piece of rotting wood. Although the basidiocarps are usually the only part of the fungus that we see, most basidiocarps only exist for a few days before they release their spores and shrivel away. The hidden mycelium may persist for years and grow to cover hundreds of acres!

Figure 8.2. Mushroom life cycle

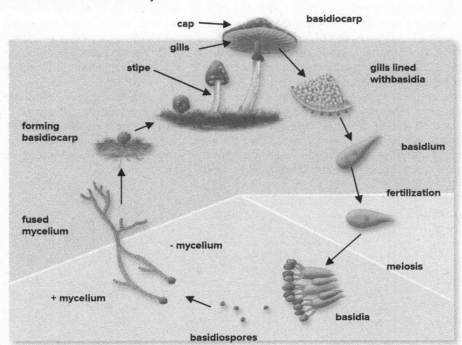

All basidiomycetes form sexually derived spores on microscopic structures called **basidia**. If the basidiomycete produces a basidiocarp, the basidia are found inside the basidiocarp; otherwise naked basidia will form directly on the vegetative hyphae.

Figure 8.2 illustrates the life cycle of a typical mushroom. Basidiospores germinate to form haploid hyphae. The hyphae of compatible strains can fuse in a manner similar to that of zygomycetes. Under moist conditions this conjoined mycelium forms a basidiocarp, the mushroom which is visible above ground. The **cap** of the mushroom has many **gills** lined with basidia. (Some basidiocarps, such as puffballs and bracket fungi, have **pores** lined with basidia instead of gills.) Inside each basidium nuclei from the two mycelia fuse to form a diploid nucleus. Meiosis occurs immediately however, and the basidiospores that form are haploid.

FUNGAL SYMBIOSIS

We have already noted that fungi are very important ecologically as saprotrophs because they help to recycle nutrients from dead organisms and fecal waste. Fungi are also important as symbiotic partners to many creatures. Recall that symbiotic relationships may be harmful to one of the partners (parasitism) or that both partners may benefit (mutualism); there are fungi that participate in either type of symbiosis. (A third type of symbiosis is possible, in which one partner benefits and the other is neither harmed nor helped, and is labeled commensalism. Mycologists have long debated whether lichens are mutualistic or commensal associations.) Fungal parasites cause such diseases as yeast and mildew infections, and plant blights, rusts, and smuts. Mutualistic fungi are found in **mycorrhizae** and **lichens**.

Mycorrhizae occur when underground plant parts (usually roots, but sometimes underground stems or other parts) become infected with non-parasitic fungi (*rhiza* is Greek for root). The mycorrhizal mycelium spreads extensively underground, nourished partly by carbohydrates produced by the plant but also saprotrophically on organic matter in the soil. Apparently plants thrive on the nutrients made available by these saprotrophs, since many species will not grow well without mycorrhizae. About 80% of all plants normally participate in mycorrhizal associations.

The simplest mycorrhizae are those which surround the root like a sheath and act like a wick to bring nutrients to the root. Since these fungi form thick mats around the roots and do not penetrate deeply into the plant tissue, they are called **ectomycorrhizae** (*ecto-* means outside). Ectomycorrhizae are common among trees and shrubs. The fungus is usually a basidiomycete, which is why you can often find groups of mushrooms around trees. Several thousand species of fungi can form ectomycorrhizae, but the types of plants that can harbor them is somewhat restricted.

Endomycorrhizae are much more common than ectomycorrhizae. Only a few species of fungi can form endomycorrhizae, but these can infect hundreds of thousands of species of plants. These fungi extend deep into the plant tissue and weave their hyphae around and even into the individual root cells. Some of the earliest fossil plants have endomycorrhizal roots, which may help to explain how these plants were able to successfully colonize the land. A single endomycorrhizal fungus may infect the roots of many different plants in a given location, connecting them all in an underground network.

Figure 8.3.   Mycorrhizae

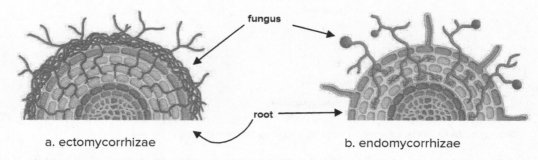

a. ectomycorrhizae   b. endomycorrhizae

A **lichen** consists of a fungus living symbiotically with photosynthetic algae amongst its hyphae. Lichens are among the first organisms to colonize inhospitable environments and help break down rock and build soil. They are important sources of food in arctic and mountain environments.

INVESTIGATIONS WITH FUNGI

In the following exercises you will examine both living and preserved fungi. Most of the structures found in the diagrams will require a microscope to see.

Investigation #1   Isolating fungi from the environment

Fungal spores are almost as ubiquitous as bacteria, and fungi can be grown from environmental samples by methods similar to those used to culture bacteria (cf. chapter 5). If the culture plate is prepared with a medium favorable to the growth of fungi and supplemented with antibiotics that kill bacteria, yeasts or mycelia should be obtained.

1. Decide what kind of environment you want to use as your source. Sample it with a sterile swab and streak the swab over a plate of rose-bengal agar. Mark the plate with your name, section, and source of inoculum and store as your instructor directs.

Period Two
1. Examine your plate for fungi. Smooth, soft, non-mycelial colonies are probably yeasts. The most common mycelia obtained by this method are actually neither zygomycetes nor basidiomycetes, but a third kind of fungus (called ascomycetes) which often produces colored spores atop a white mycelium.

Investigation #2   Conjugation in zygomycetes

Individual members of any particular species of zygomycete are pretty much identical – there are no obvious differences one could describe as "male" or "female." For this reason the terms "male" and "female" are not used with zygomycetes. Instead, species are divided into + and - mating strains. When a species is first discovered the designation of which strain is + and which is - is arbitrary. When new strains are discovered, they are classified as + or - depending on which known strains they can mate with.
1. Look at a culture plate containing + and - strains of the zygomycete *Phycomyces blakesleanus*. See if you can find zygospores where the mycelia meet. (The long hairy projections are asexual sporangia.) Look at the plate under a dissecting microscope to see the zygospores in more detail. Is there a pattern to where they form? Which strains can mate with which?
2. Examine a prepared slide of *Rhizopus*. Look for zygospores and asexual sporangia. How do they compare?

Investigation #3   Basidiocarp structure

Basidiocarps are made of packed hyphae. A mushroom starts out as a small ball or lump of hyphae. The central portion quickly elongates into a **stipe** that raises the cap off of the ground. As the cap unfolds the gills become exposed to air currents which disperse the spores.
1. **Gills and basidia**: Look at a cross-section of a cap of the mushroom *Coprinus*. Locate the basidia lining the gills. Examine a basidium under high power and see how the basidiospores are attached. How is this different from zygospores?
2. **Pores**: A variety of basidiomycetes is on display: puffballs, stinkhorns, etc. Pay careful attention to the puffballs and bracket fungi and locate the pores these basidiocarps have instead of gills.

Investigation #4   Fungal symbiosis
1. **Mycorrhizae**: Compare prepared slides of ecto- and endomycorrhizae. Examine the relationship between the hyphae and the plant tissue in each kind of mycorrhizae.
2. **Lichens**: Many different dried lichens are on display. The symbiosis can have a profound effect on the form of the fungus – how do these lichens compare to the other fungi you have observed?

Important Terms

basidiocarp
basidiomycete
basidium
cap
chitin
conjugation
ectomycorrhiza
endomycorrhiza
gill
hypha
lichen
mycorrhiza
mycelium
pore
sporangium
stipe
zygomycete
zygospore

CHAPTER 9
THE ORIGIN OF LAND PLANTS

INTRODUCTION

Half a billion years ago, life existed only in the seas — there are no fossils of any terrestrial organisms from before that time. The oceans were full of bacteria, protists, and fungi. In addition, various aquatic animals such as worms, squid, and even fish had evolved, as we shall see in chapter 12. However, there were no plants. The only photosynthetic creatures (other than bacteria) were the different kinds of algae. Eventually some algae developed characteristics which enabled them to survive on dry land. These became the first plants, and all modern plants appear to have descended from them. Many modern plants live in water, but they retain some of the basic features that originally allowed plants to live on land. As animals, humans tend to think of plants as "primitive" organisms, but the plant kingdom is actually the youngest of the kingdoms of life. Once plants brought the power of photosynthesis to dry land, animals and fungi were able to follow; until that had happened only the water was habitable. The origin of plants is thus one of the critical events in the history of life on earth.

When scientists reconstruct the evolutionary history of life they occasionally run into gaps where, due to a lack of fossils or intermediate species, it is difficult to say how some transition occurred. Not so with the origin of plants: In the modern world there exists a continuum of numerous species of algae that blend fairly smoothly into the simplest plants. In fact, botanists sometimes argue about exactly where the algae end and the plants begin.

TWO KINDS OF GREEN ALGAE

As we have seen, it is possible to perform photosynthesis with different kinds of chlorophyll (algae can have chlorophyll *a* plus *b* or *c*) and accessory pigments (carotenoids or phycobilins). The carbohydrates made in photosynthesis can be used to make starch or cellulose, or many unusual compounds, such as agar or carrageenin. It happens that all modern plants have the same kind of photosynthesis, possess chlorophylls *a* and *b*, store carbohydrates as starch, and make their cell walls out of cellulose. This implies that their algal ancestors also had these characteristics. You should recall that the green algae of Division Chlorophyta have all of these traits.

Figure 9.1.   The relationship between land plants and various algae

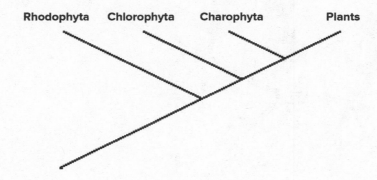

You should also remember that like the green algae, red algae have chloroplasts that arose from cyanobacteria directly by primary endosymbiosis. It turns out that the DNA from both the nuclei and chloroplasts of red and green algae are similar, indicating that they share a common ancestor that had chloroplasts. Since red algal chloroplasts are more like cyanobacteria than those of green algae, it would seem that red algae are more like the common ancestor than green algae. Does this mean that evolution went from red algae to green algae to plants? Almost — it turns out that the link between chlorophyte green algae and plants is not quite so direct.

Charophytes are part of the smooth transition between the chlorophytes and true land plants (there is actually another group of algae between the chlorophytes and charophytes, but we will ignore them here). They have most of the characteristics of Division Chlorophyta and can be considered a special type of green algae. But they also share several biochemical and genetic characteristics with land plants, along with a specific pattern of mitosis. Botanists debate whether the charophytes should be included within the plant kingdom; indeed, the boundaries of the plant kingdom are quite a matter of dispute. Those who exclude the charophytes call the kingdom "Plantae." Others say that plants and charophytes together constitute a kingdom named "Streptophyta," while another faction would set the boundary to include even the chlorophytes and call the kingdom "Viridiplantae." Some would even include the red algae in a kingdom named "Archaeplastida!" In truth, the relationships between these groups is close enough that there is no clear way to draw lines between them.

In any event, the charophytes are an old and diverse line of evolution in their own right, and exhibit a range of morphological types. One genus, *Chara*, is especially interesting in relation to plant evolution.

The body of *Chara* is quite different from any green alga in that it is organized into **nodes** and **internodes**. Nodes are regions of the organism where branching occurs and internodes are the long straight sections between the nodes (figure 9.2). Plants are arranged in the same way: their stems and branches are internodes and the points where branches or leaves occur are nodes. This structure results from a special pattern of growth called **apical growth**, a pattern *Chara* also shares with plants.

Figure 9.2. *Chara*, showing nodes and internodes

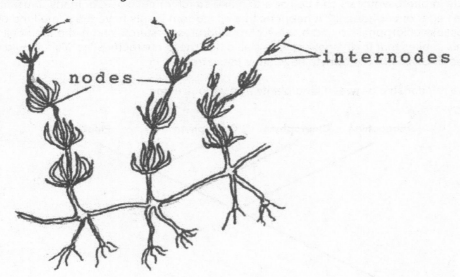

Drawing by John Dickerman

Apical growth is a deceptively simple concept which often confuses people, who sometimes seem to think that the new growth of a plant emerges from the ground, pushing older tissues skyward (this is often how plant growth is represented in cartoons). In fact, new growth in plants occurs only at the very tips of the stems, branches, and roots. The part of the plant nearest the ground is the oldest and never grows longer once it is mature. New tissues are formed by cell division, and this only takes place at the apexes of the shoots.

Nodes, internodes, and apical growth explain why plants look the way they do – thin and branching rather than having a concise and symmetrical form like animals do. However this pattern of growth probably had little to do with the ability of plants to survive on land. On the other hand, another feature plants share with *Chara* was crucial in this regard: the presence of sterile, protective cells around the sperm and eggs.

In algae eggs are produced inside specialized cells called oogonia and sperm are produced in cells called **antheridia** (since eggs and sperm are both gametes, oogonia and antheridia are sometimes called gametangia). The actual oogonium or antheridium surrounding the gametes is made of the cell wall and associated material left over from the progenitor cell – it is not very large or thick. However, in *Chara* the oogonia are surrounded by spiral filaments of non-reproductive cells, cells which cannot by themselves produce eggs. This extra layer of protection is probably not very important for the charophytes, since most algae are able to survive quite well without it. On the other hand, it turns out to be crucial for land plants. Even in the simplest land plants this extra layer of cells has developed into a structure that not only protects the egg but also holds the zygote after fertilization and keeps the young embryo from drying out.

This is an interesting illustration of an important concept in evolution. It is apparent that this protective layer around the oogonium arose <u>before</u> it was most needed (that is, in aquatic organisms like charophytes). Actually, evolution has to work this way. There is no way an organism in a new environment can suddenly create the adaptations it needs. It will only survive if it <u>already</u> has them in some form. The presence of these structures is what allows the organism to successfully exploit the new environment. The new structures arise within the ancestral population via the natural processes that give rise to variation in populations as discussed in chapter 2. Structures which arise in one environment but become the basis for adaptations to another environment have been called preadaptations. Despite the name, preadaptations do not imply any kind of "planning" by an organism. Rather, they are simply existing variations that are co-opted for some new use. Because of this most biologists prefer the term **exaptation** to preadaptation.

ADAPTATIONS TO TERRESTRIAL ENVIRONMENTS

Ecologically, the major difference between plants and algae is that plants live on land. This presented two problems to early plants: support and desiccation. A fifty foot long kelp does not have to be very strong structurally because its body is constantly supported by water. On the other hand, land plants are constantly struggling against gravity. Only those that have developed stiff fibers in their bodies (such as wood) have been able to grow very large.

Desiccation is a more formidable problem. All life depends on water. Aquatic organisms are seldom in danger of drying out, but terrestrial creatures must obtain water from some source and, more importantly, avoid losing the water that they do obtain. All plants are covered by a **cuticle,** a layer of wax which seals in moisture. Without a cuticle plants would never have been able to move inland. Cuticles are also present in a genus of charophyte called *Coleochaete*. Like the oogonia of *Chara*, the cuticles of *Coleochaete* are not very important for aquatic living. Again, this is an example of a exaptation.

The availability of water also influences sexual reproduction, since sperm cells must be able to swim to eggs to create zygotes. In terrestrial animals males deliver sperm to the eggs during copulation, but this is not an option for plants rooted in place. Plants use **alternation of generations** to deal with this problem.

With alternation of generations, <u>a diploid organism gives rise to a haploid organism and a haploid organism gives rise to a diploid organism</u>. To understand how different this is from animal reproduction, pretend for a moment that you are a product of alternation of generations. Assume your mother was a normal diploid person. She would produce normal, haploid eggs. Now imagine that, instead of being fertilized, one of those eggs grew directly into you! All of the cells in your body would be haploid. You would have no father. Genetically, you would only be half of what your mother was. You would not require meiosis in order to make sperm or eggs, since all of your cells are already haploid. You would mate with another haploid individual but then have diploid children. Your mother would not see her normal chromosome number restored until her grandchildren were born, and you would not see another haploid generation until your own grandchildren were born. The two chromosome numbers alternate.

Among plants (some protists also alternate generations) the haploid members of a species look quite different from the diploid members. Although this makes the life cycle look complex, it at least makes it easy to tell who is haploid and who is diploid. Diploid plants make asexual spores that have thick walls to protect them from dehydration. These spores are shed to the wind and dispersed. Those that land in a suitable environment germinate into haploid plants. The haploid plants will produce gametes for sexual reproduction. As a result, the haploid plants are generally small and limited to moist environments, since the sperm must swim from one plant to another. Diploid plants are called **sporophytes** because they produce spores. Similarly haploid plants are called **gametophytes**. Sporophytes may be either small or large (grass and trees are both sporophytes) but gametophytes are always small. *Chara* does not alternate generations, but some other charophytes and green algae do. Presumably the common ancestor of charophytes and land plants became extinct long ago.

Summary of Plant Characteristics and their Evolution

Features found in the Chlorophyta:
- chlorophylls *a* and *b*
- starch as major carbohydrate
- cellulose cell walls

Additional features found in *Chara*:
- sterile jackets around reproductive cells
- body made of nodes and internodes
- apical growth

Additional features found in *Coleochaete*:
- waxy cuticle

Additional features not found in *Chara*:
- alternation of generations

NON-VASCULAR PLANTS

Although the plant kingdom seems to be a single line of evolution from the charophytes, it must have diverged quickly. Most plant sporophytes contain **vascular tissue**, which helps them move food and water throughout their bodies. Three small divisions do not have vascular tissue. They are the simplest plants: **liverworts**, **hornworts**, and **mosses** (Divisions Hepatophyta, Anthocerophyta, and Bryophyta, respectively). The mosses are somewhat more complex than the other two groups, but all lack true roots, stems, leaves, flowers, fruits, and seeds. Their sporophytes are small plants, since they do not have vascular tissue to carry water very far from the ground. Indeed, these are the only plants whose sporophytes are smaller than their gametophytes.

Liverworts get their name from the fact that they grow dichotomously into lobes, producing a shape which must have reminded someone of a liver (*wort* is an old Anglo-Saxon word for herb). This makes their bodies look leafy, but these structures are not true leaves because they have no vascular tissue. Likewise, liverworts are not anchored to the ground by roots but by simple analogs called rhizoids.

Hornworts look similar to liverworts. In hornworts, as in all plants, both gametangia are surrounded by sterile cells. The female gametangium is called an **archegonium** instead of an oogonium, because it is larger and more complex than an algal oogonium and because it continues to hold the zygote after fertilization (the male gametangium is still called an antheridium).

Figure 9.3. hornwort

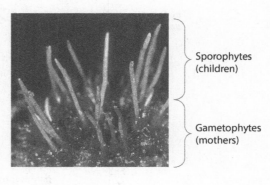

Sporophytes (children)

Gametophytes (mothers)

© Steven P. Lynch

Young plant sporophytes are always rooted in their gametophyte mothers. If the sporophyte grows much larger than the gametophyte, it eventually destroys the gametophyte. On the other hand, if the gametophyte is larger than the sporophyte, as it is in hornworts and liverworts, the two live harmoniously. The gametangia of hornworts are imbedded in the upper surface of the leaflike body of the plant. When the hornwort sporophyte grows out of the archegonium it looks like it is growing on top of the gametophyte. The sporophyte is tall and slender and looks like a horn, hence the name of the taxon.

Mosses are more complex than either hornworts or liverworts. Some species can grow to be over a foot tall and contain a crude form of vascular tissue which is analogous to that found in true vascular plants. The basic moss body consists of a slender "leafy" axis anchored by rhizoids to the soil. Despite their size and complexity, these plants are haploid gametophytes. At the top of mature plants archegonia or antheridia form. The sperm are released amidst rain or heavy dew to swim towards an archegonium; occasionally raindrops will splash the sperm directly onto the archegonium and shorten the journey. The fertilized zygote develops in a manner similar to that of a hornwort: a long stalk growing on top of the established gametophyte. When the sporophyte reaches its mature length it develops an enlarged sporangium full of haploid spores. The life cycle is diagrammed in figure 9.4.

Figure 9.4. Life cycle of a moss.

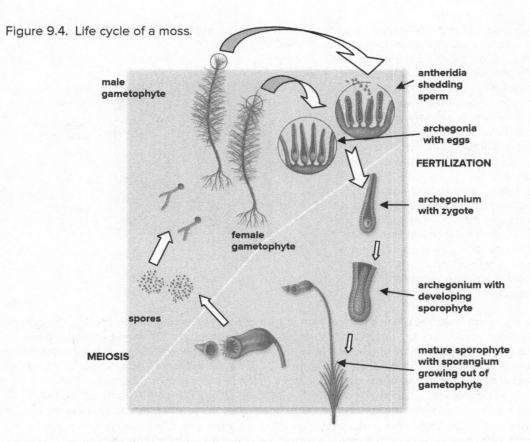

male gametophyte

antheridia shedding sperm

archegonia with eggs

FERTILIZATION

archegonium with zygote

female gametophyte

archegonium with developing sporophyte

spores

mature sporophyte with sporangium growing out of gametophyte

MEIOSIS

Sphagnum is an unusual genus of moss. It grows in thick mats on bogs. The water under the growing moss in a bog is so thickly covered that it has little oxygen. The *Sphagnum* also makes the water slightly acidic, which retards the growth of bacteria. As a result, organic materials have been found in bogs that have been preserved for centuries with minimal decay. Because *Sphagnum* has specialized cells for storing water, it is often used in horticulture as a moist medium for germinating seeds. Structurally, *Sphagnum* is different from most mosses, so we will not consider it in detail beyond noting its ecological and economic importance.

VASCULAR PLANTS

Although mosses are fairly common, they are seldom noticed by most people. Their life cycles are dominated by the gametophyte generation, and the mechanics of sexual reproduction in plants limit gametophytes to damp habitats and small statures. The plants we generally concern ourselves with are vascular plants. These are sporophytes, which are free to colonize dry environments and grow to tremendous heights. Due to alternation of generations, the spores of vascular sporophytes do not germinate into other sporophytes but rather into tiny gametophytes. The gametophytes of vascular plants are smaller than liverworts, often even microscopic, and are not easy to find. They reproduce sexually and die giving birth to a new generation of sporophytes.

In plants large size is due to the presence of vascular tissue. It is this tissue that transports material throughout the body of the plant, bringing groundwater up to the leafy crown and photosynthetically produced carbohydrates underground to the roots. It also forms the woody skeleton that supports the plant.

The vascular tissue of plants is analogous to the vascular tissue of animals – that is, the circulatory system. Both transport materials throughout the organism's body. However, the vascular system in plants is not closed and does not circulate; it consists of two separate conduction systems. **Xylem** carries water up from the roots to the leaves where it constantly evaporates into the air. It is because this system is open and continuously losing moisture that plants need so much water to survive. **Phloem** brings carbohydrates from photosynthetic and storage cells to other tissues where it is consumed.

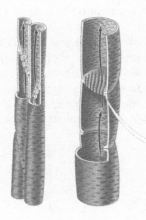

Figure 9.5. Xylem cells

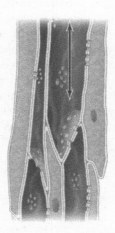

Figure 9.6. Phloem cells

Both xylem and phloem are complex tissues composed of several types of specialized cells. In each case the functional cells are long and thin, like tubes. Xylem cell are dead at maturity and work like simple pipes. Wood is made up of layers of old xylem (xylem comes from the Greek word *xylon,* which means wood). Phloem is somewhat more complex than xylem. When phloem dies it ceases to function and must be replaced. Long-lived plants such as trees produce new phloem each year in a ring around the xylem, and old worn-out phloem builds up as bark. If the thin layer of functioning phloem is killed, the entire plant will die with it.

Most vascular plants reproduce by seeds. Seeds are a complex variation on alternation of generations and will be described further in the next chapter. The first vascular plants did not make seeds. Their modern descendants comprise several divisions of the plant kingdom. We will look at two of these groups.

The oldest known fossil of a vascular plant is about 420 million years old. It is of a small plant which lacks roots and leaves – it is nothing but a stem. From such plants eventually arose the **lycopods** (Division Lycophyta): plants with true leaves and roots supplied with vascular tissue. At one time lycopods were very common. Coal was formed from decaying forests of huge treelike lycopods. All the tree lycopods are now extinct, but about 1,000 herbaceous species still exist.

Some species of lycopods are frequently found growing on the floor of coniferous forests. They have small spiky leaves, giving rise to the common name "ground pine." These plants are sporophytes. Their gametophytes are small, subterranean, and dependent on mycorrhizal fungi for nutrition. When a lycopod sporophyte is mature it bears densely-leafed branches called **strobili**. Each leaf of the strobilus is a sporangium full of spores, so they are relatively thick. The entire strobilus looks like a small soft club, suggesting another common name, "club moss" (they are, of course, not true mosses).

Lycopods are not limited to moist environments like mosses and liverworts. In fact, some species of the genus *Selaginella* are adapted to very dry environments, like the "resurrection plant" which shrivels into a dormant state when dry but quickly revives when wet again.

As with the lycopods, **ferns** (Division Pterophyta) were once more common than they are now. However, ferns have been more successful than the lycopods and about 12,000 species are alive today. The fern life cycle is similar to that of the lycopods and is illustrated in figure 9.7.

Fern gametophytes are small and heart-shaped. They are photosynthetic organisms, growing on top of the ground (fern spores usually require light to germinate), but may also have mycorrhizae. In most species the gametophyte bears both antheridia and archegonia. A zygote develops inside the gametophyte archegonium and grows into a mature sporophyte as the gametophyte dies. Fern gametophytes were originally called "prothallia" since they were known to give rise to the vascular body (called a thallus) before all of the details of alternation of generations were worked out.

The young sporophyte grows into a thick vascular **rhizome** (horizontal stem) and begins to sprout leaves. Fern leaves begin as curled up structures called **fiddleheads** (because of their shape) and unfurl as they grow. Fern leaves are usually much larger than lycopod leaves. Most ferns do not produce strobili but instead bear spores on the undersides of their leaves in small umbrella-shaped structures called **sori**. Although fern gametophytes tend to look alike, fern sporophytes are morphologically quite diverse. They can range from tiny aquatic plants less than a centimeter long to 100-foot tall tropical tree ferns.

Figure 9.7. Typical fern life cycle

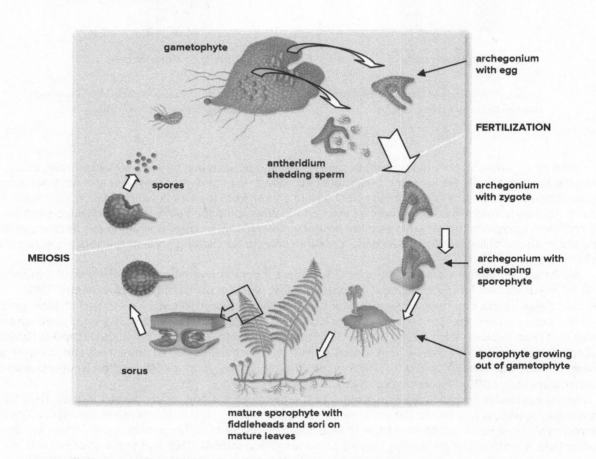

INVESTIGATIONS WITH SIMPLE PLANTS

In the following exercises you will view a variety of prepared slides. Preserved and living specimens will also be available. In all of the plants the gametophytes are quite different from the sporophytes; take the time to learn which ones go together so that you can fully understand how alternation of generations works.

Investigation #1   Special *Chara* structures
1.   **Morphology**: Examine a preserved specimen of *Chara*. Identify the nodes and internodes and compare the algal body to that of more familiar plants.
2.   **Oogonia**: Examine a prepared slide of *Chara* oogonia and study the spiral filaments surrounding the egg.

Investigation #2   Non-vascular plant structures
1.   **Hornworts**: Study the preserved specimens of the hornwort *Anthoceros*. Note the slender sporophyte growing up from the gametophyte like a horn. Remember that the sporophyte is a separate, genetically distinct organism growing on top of the gametophyte. Then look at a prepared slide of a sporophyte and identify the spores inside.
2.   **Mosses**: Observe the preserved specimens of *Polytrichum* and identify the sporophytes attached to the gametophytes. Again, the sporophyte is a separate organism growing on top of the gametophyte. Preserved *Sphagnum* is also on display. The small dark spherical bodies are the sporophytes.

Investigation #3   Morphology of vascular cells
1.   Obtain a prepared slide of macerated wood. This is xylem which has been treated so that the cells are separated. Observe the thin tubular shape of the cells and compare with the less specialized plant cells you have observed in other plants. Look for pores in the cell walls that allow water to pass from cell to cell.

Investigation #4   Lycopod structures
1.   Study living or preserved *Lycopodium*. Identify the strobili and study one under the microscope.
2.   Examine the preserved lycopod gametophyte. Does it look at all like the sporophyte?
3.   Look at a cross section of a lycopod stem (either *Lycopodium* or *Selaginella*). Study the vascular tissue in the center. The large central cells are xylem. Phloem cells form a ring around the xylem. How much of the stem is vascular tissue?

Investigation #5   Fern structures
1.   Survey the various fern sporophytes on display and compare their shapes. Look for fiddleheads and sori.
2.   Look at the prepared slides of gametophytes. Compare the gametophytes to the fern sporophytes and also to the lycopod gametophyte. Identify the archegonia and antheridia and observe how the young sporophyte grows out of the archegonium.

Important Terms

alternation of generations
antheridium
apical growth
archegonium
charophyte
cuticle
fern
fiddlehead
gametophyte
hornwort
internode
liverwort
lycopod
moss
node
phloem
rhizome
sorus
sporophyte
strobilus
vascular tissue
xylem

CHAPTER 10
SEED PLANTS

INTRODUCTION

In the last chapter we looked at several types of seedless plants. You may have felt that all of these plants were unusual. That is because most familiar plants have seeds. Three hundred million years ago, this was not the case – the dominant forms of plant life were lycopods and ferns. But a lot can happen in three hundred million years. Not only did seeds develop, they took over the world. Today we define most of the earth's environments, from grasslands to tropical forests, by the kinds of seed plants they contain.

SEEDS

A seed turns out to be a relatively complex structure. We can best understand what it is by comparing seed plants to spore plants. Recall that the gametophytes of ferns and lycopods are small and normally hidden. The prominent form of these plants is the sporophyte. And of course the sporophyte reproduces via spores. Is the seed, then, homologous to the spore? The answer is both yes and no.

Many sporophytes produce a single type of spore. This germinates into a gametophyte which may be male, female, or both (bisexual); different species work in different ways. In some species, however, the sporophyte produces two types of spores: large megaspores and small microspores. Megaspores always grow into female gametophytes and microspores always grow into male gametophytes.

Seed plants produce megaspores and microspores. But there is an added twist: In seed plants the sporangium containing the megaspore is wrapped up in a layer of specialized leaves. This extra layer is called an **integument.** A sporangium containing a megaspore and surrounded by an integument is called an **ovule** (figure 10.1). Since ovules turn into seeds, part of the seed is homologous to a megaspore. But there's more.

In ferns and lycopods, spores are released from their sporangia and are carried away by wind or water. They germinate into gametophytes some distance away from the parent sporophyte. But in a seed plant the sporangium is sealed by the integument and the megaspore is trapped inside. Therefore, the megaspore germinates <u>inside the ovule</u>. Thus part of the seed is homologous to the female gametophyte.

Figure 10.1. Seed development from the ovule

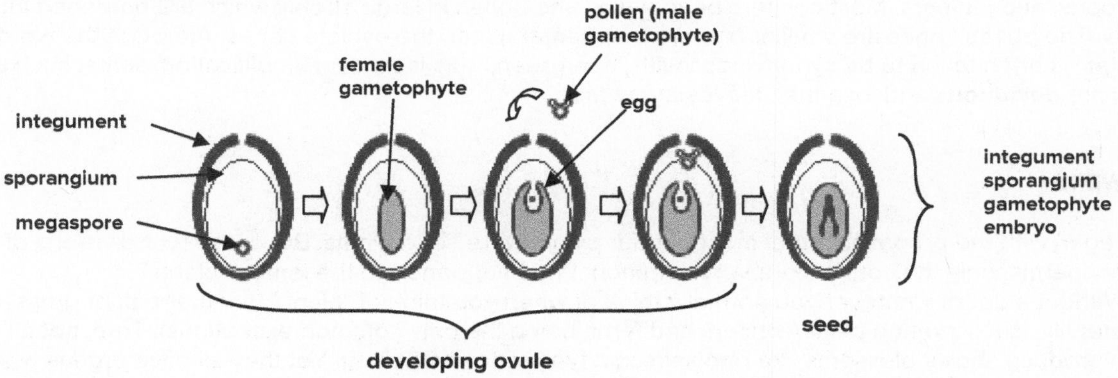

Where is the male gametophyte during all of this? It starts out as a microspore in a different sporangium. The microspore grows into a tiny gametophyte called **pollen.** The pollen finds its way to a minute opening in the integument of an ovule. There it grows through the sporangium and into the archegonium of the female gametophyte. At this point fertilization occurs and the embryo of a new sporophyte starts to grow inside the gametophyte. An ovule which contains a gametophyte which contains an embryo is a **seed.** The seed is actually an entire family in one small package: parent (sporophyte ovule), daughter (female gametophyte), and grandchild (new sporophyte embryo).

To summarize: The visible seed plant is a sporophyte. It produces a female gametophyte offspring inside an ovule. When the gametophyte mates with pollen an embryo grows inside the gametophyte. The combination of ovule, gametophyte, and embryo (three generations) is a seed.

GYMNOSPERMS

Seeds first appear in the fossil record in rocks about 350 million years old. At that time ferns and lycopods were forming the great forests of the Carboniferous Period. Over the following 100 million years seed plants became more and more common, so that by the time dinosaurs appeared, they had largely replaced the seedless plants. The oldest known plants that had seeds are called seed ferns. It is not clear how closely related seed ferns are to modern ferns, but they look similar.

Seed ferns are now extinct, as are several other groups of primitive seed plants. Today there are five divisions of seed plants: **angiosperms, conifers**, gnetophytes, cycads, and the unique tree called *Ginkgo*. Angiosperms differ from the other four divisions because they grow their seeds inside a special organ called a carpel. We will return to them later. The other seed plants are referred to as "**gymnosperms**" because their seeds are not inside a carpel (gymnosperm comes from the Greek *gymnos,* naked, and *sperma,* seed).

Most gymnosperms are large plants or trees. Conifers are quite common, but other gymnosperms are not widely distributed. The most unusual are the gnetophytes; they are almost never encountered by most people. Cycads were common in the age of the dinosaurs but are much rarer now and they are seldom found outside of tropical or subtropical environments. Ginkgos are an ancient group of trees but only one species is left. It is an oriental tree currently found wild only in eastern China; even there it is rare. It has traditionally been cultivated in the temple gardens of Japan and is now used as an ornamental all over the world.

The familiar conifers (Division Coniferophyta) are the only gymnosperms which form large forests. Unlike the cycads, conifers are well adapted to cold climates and short growing seasons. There are only about 550 species of conifers; some of the better known groups are the pines and spruces, yews, redwoods, and junipers. Most conifers bear ovules and pollen in large strobili which are hardened into **cones.** The pollen cones are smaller and more ephemeral than the ovulate cones. Although the word "conifer" is often taken to be synonymous with "evergreen," this is an oversimplification: some, such as the larch, are **deciduous** and lose their leaves every fall.

FLOWERS

We began with the proposition that most familiar plants were seed plants. But of the four divisions of gymnosperms, only the conifers are very common. What happened to the familiar plants?

Without a doubt whatever you normally think of when you think of "plant," whether oak or grass, cactus or water lily, is a flowering plant (conifers and ferns being the only common exceptions). True, not all of these produce showy blossoms like one sees in a typical flower garden. Yet they all have organs which are structurally and functionally homologous to the brightly colored flowers of roses, violets, carnations, or what have you. They all have flowers with **carpels**. Flowering plants are grouped in the single Division Anthophyta, but it is a huge division with about 300,000 species.

So far the story of plant evolution has been one of surrounding reproductive structures in new layers of tissue. In the charophytes sterile cells surrounded the eggs; these became the archegonia in land plants. In gymnosperms, an integument surrounded the megasporangium to form an ovule. The carpel continues this trend, as it is another special leaf which surrounds the ovule. In ovulate pine cones seeds are borne on the individual leaves (scales) of the cone. Now imagine that those leaves spread out and wrapped around the seeds – then you would have a carpel. One or more carpels fused together form a **pistil**, which is in the center of most flowers. The word "angiosperm" comes from the Greek *angion,* vessel, and *sperma,* seed, reflecting the fact that angiosperm seeds are contained within a vessel formed by the carpels.

The oldest fossil flowers date from the Cretaceous Period, about 140 million years ago. At that time the giant lycopods and seed ferns were extinct and conifers and cycads dominated the landscape. It is unclear why the first carpels were an improvement over the gymnosperms; perhaps they protected the seeds from being eaten by insects. For whatever reason, flowers were a success. The angiosperms diversified greatly after the Cretaceous and have been the earth's major form of plant life for the past 70 million years.

Flowers come in many shapes and sizes, but they all follow a basic pattern. In the center is the **pistil** (figure 10.2)**.** Made of one or more carpels, the pistil is essentially a curled up leaf (or several fused leaves) containing the ovules. Pollen lands on the top of the pistil and must grow down through it in order to reach the ovules within the ovary. Surrounding the pistil are the **stamens**. The stamens are highly modified leaves with bulbous tips, similar to the spore-filled leaves of a lycopod strobilus. This is where the microspores develop into pollen. Around the stamens is a ring of more normal-looking leaves, often brightly colored, called **petals**. Finally there is another ring of leaves, the **sepals.** The specialized leaves outside the stamens provide one advantage of flowers: They attract insects and other animals, either by color, scent, or by secreting nectar, and the animals carry pollen to new flowers in the process. This tends to be more efficient than wind pollination. A flower which has all four parts is called **perfect. Imperfect** flowers lack one or more of these parts. For example, some plants have pistils and stamens in separate flowers. The pistillate flowers lack stamens and the staminate flowers lack pistils. Other imperfect flowers may lack petals or sepals.

Figure 10.2. Basic flower structure

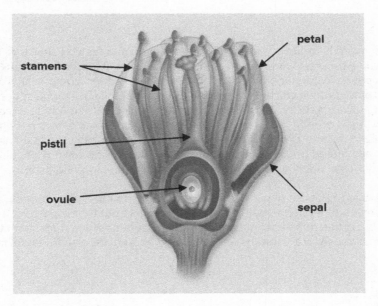

Many angiosperms bear their flowers singly, as does the familiar rose. Often flowers are borne in clusters. A floral cluster is called an **inflorescence**. Inflorescence types are species-specific traits and are important in identifying and classifying plants. There are many types of inflorescences, but we will only mention two common, but complex, types: **catkins** and **capitulums**.

Catkins are only produced by certain trees. A catkin is a very short branch covered with small flowers (figure 10.3). The flowers are always unisexual, so catkins can be said to be either pistillate or staminate. A capitulum is an inflorescence that looks like a single flower. In fact, they are often called **composite** flowers. Daisies, sunflowers, asters, zinnias, and chrysanthemums are all composites. Each "petal" of a daisy is really an entire flower (figure 10.4). These are called ray flowers since they radiate out from the central disc. The disc is usually covered with numerous tiny flowers called disc flowers. Plants with composite flowers belong to the family Asteraceae, which, with some 20,000 species, is the largest family of vascular plants.

Figure 10.3. Catkin

Figure 10.4. Capitulum structure

© Steven P. Lynch

ray flowers

disc flowers

Pixtal/AGE Fotostock

FRUITS

When an angiosperm ovule is fertilized, it develops into a seed in a fashion similar to that of gymnosperms. Meanwhile, the pistil also develops. It enlarges and changes form. It becomes a **fruit**. A simple fruit is a developed pistil with seeds inside (figure 10.5). Many fruits have added complexities, such as additional tissues joining to the pistil, but we will not consider that in any detail. The modifications found in fruits usually are important aids to mobility. Some fruits have hooks or barbs so that they can be carried by animals. Others are winged or fluffy and can ride the wind for miles. Still others become fleshy and are quickly eaten by birds. Many seeds can survive intact inside the digestive tracts of birds and germinate when they are finally eliminated (there are some species whose seeds will not germinate until they have passed through a bird!). This mobility has played a major role in helping angiosperms colonize new environments.

Sometimes people argue about whether a particular food, for example a tomato, is really a fruit or a vegetable. In common usage these terms have no real meaning, but to the botanist a fruit is a developed pistil containing seeds. By this definition, many common "vegetables" are fruits: tomatoes, green peppers, cucumbers, pumpkins, squash, green beans, etc. Nuts and acorns are also fruits. As fruits they all start out as flowers.

Figure 10.5. Fruits

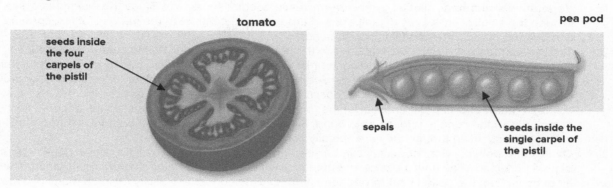

INVESTIGATIONS WITH SEED PLANTS

Investigation #1   Growing plants from seeds

An essential part of becoming a biologist is gaining experience and confidence in working with living things. This usually means that you need to be able to grow and care for the organism you are studying. In the following exercise, you will have a chance to grow in a greenhouse plants you start from seeds. You will have to maintain the plant through several stages of development over several weeks. Your plant will be a source of live material to examine stems, leaves, roots, flowers, and seeds. Since different groups will be raising different species, the class as a whole will encounter many patterns and rates of growth. You may therefore find it instructive to compare your plant's development to that of the others.

1.   You will work in pairs to cut down on the number of plants in the greenhouse. Fill a 4" pot with artificial potting medium. The top of the medium should be about 1 cm below the top of the pot – this allows adequate space for watering. Moisten the medium and make 3-4 small holes in the surface, about 1 cm deep. Place a seed in each hole and cover it over. (If you are using grass seed, do not bury the seed but simply sow it on top of the soil.) Use only one type of seed. <u>Do not waste seeds by sowing more than four in a pot</u>. When the plants are established, you will remove the smallest plants and raise only the biggest, healthiest plant.

2.   Water the medium <u>thoroughly</u>. Place a label with your names, class section, and the species of your plant in the pot and place the pot where your instructor directs.

3.   You will make observations of the plant's development weekly, and record your observations in a short journal. Among the things you should include in your journal:

   • Planting date. Include a brief description of the dry seed.

   • Approximate time of germination. This will vary from a few days to more than a week.

   • The appearance of the young seedling, <u>especially the shape and number of leaves that first appear</u>.

   • The time the first foliage leaves appear. How do they differ from the first leaves on the seedling (if they differ at all)?

   • As more foliage leaves develop, note the areas of growth, the internode length, and arrangement of leaves.

   • Watch for the development of new structures, such as buds and flowers.

Investigation #2   Conifer structures

1. **Vegetative structures**: Not all gymnosperms have needles for leaves. Study the examples which include the small scaly leaves of junipers and arborvitae. In contrast to the needles of firs, spruces, and other conifers, pine needles grow in bundles.

2. **Cones**: Compare the small pollen cones to the larger ovulate cones. Pollen cones are produced yearly and wither shortly after shedding their pollen. Ovulate cones take up to three years to mature. During this time both female and male (i.e., pollen, blown in from a pollen cone) gametophytes grow within the cone before fertilization finally occurs. A demonstration of pine development is also on display. Finally, examine the unusual juniper cones. The scales of these small cones become fleshy at maturity so the cone is swollen and round. Since juniper cones are often brightly colored, they are called "berries" even though they are actually cones.

3. **Ovules and pollen**: Conifer ovules can be seen on prepared slides of ovulate cones. Look at a slide of pine pollen and see how a pair of air bubbles gives each grain a heart-shaped appearance. These air bubbles help the pollen float through the air to ovulate cones. The sticky resin on many ovulate cones functions to catch airborne pollen and "glue" it to the ovulate cone.

Investigation #3   Angiosperm structures

You will be given one or more flowers to dissect. The exact kind will depend upon availability at the time of the lab. You will need to use a dissecting microscope to see many of the structures clearly. Start with a simple flower and then look at flowers from a capitulum.

1. First examine the whole flower without a microscope. Is it symmetrical or asymmetrical? Asymmetrical flowers are often highly modified. Next determine whether your flower is perfect or imperfect. Be careful – one phenomenon which confuses things is fusion, in which two parts appear to be one. Try to identify all of the parts in figure 10.2. Count the number of petals, stamens, and pistils. In most species these numbers are constant and therefore useful taxonomically.

2. Pull off the petals on one side and examine the flower under the dissecting microscope. Identify the stamens and pistil(s).

3. Repeat the dissection with a disc flower and a ray flower from a capitulum. The parts of the ray flower are very small and located in a tube at the base.

4. Many other flowers are on display, including several catkins. Compare them to the flowers you have just dissected.

5. Survey the various fruits on display. Compare them to the flowers you have studied.

Important Terms

angiosperm
capitulum
carpel
catkin
composite flower
cone
conifer
deciduous
fruit
gymnosperm
imperfect
inflorescence
integument
ovule
perfect
petal
pistil
pollen
seed
sepal
stamen

CHAPTER 11
IDENTIFICATION KEYS
AND PLANT MORPHOLOGY

INTRODUCTION

We have stressed that taxonomy is valuable because it organizes a vast amount of data about millions of different species. If one knows the scientific name of an organism and where it fits in the overall taxonomic scheme, it is a fairly simple matter to look up information concerning that organism. However, identifying an organism in the first place can be a formidable problem, especially if the specimen was collected in the field.

KEYS

One of the most important jobs of the taxonomist is to construct **keys**. A key is basically a table of characteristics found within a group of organisms, arranged so that the characteristics become an index to the various organisms treated in the key. A good key should be **dichotomous** – that is, at any given branch point in the key there should only be two choices, so that you only have to decide whether your specimen belongs on one branch of the key or the other (keys with more than two choices per branching point are very difficult to use, and the whole point to a key is to make identification easy). The best keys have several characteristics listed at each branching point so that they can be used even on specimens that are damaged or do not exhibit all of the normal characteristics of the taxon.

Although keys may look like classification systems, they are not – keys are used strictly for identification. Unlike keys, classification systems need not be, and seldom are, dichotomous (for example, we divide eukaryotes into several kingdoms, not just two). Moreover, keys do not differentiate analogous from homologous structures. Thus all organisms with a particular trait will follow the same branch of a key even if that trait has multiple evolutionary origins. (For example, in the following key *Ginkgo* is separated from the other gymnosperms and placed among the angiosperms simply because of its leaf shape.)

Keys have been constructed for most groups of organisms; many different keys of varying quality have been published in small paperback books designed to be carried into the field by both amateur and professional naturalists. A single key will only cover a particular kind of organism (for example trees, wildflowers, insects, or birds) and is often restricted to a particular geographic region – otherwise the key would be huge and unwieldy.

KEYING OUT AN ORGANISM

The process of using a key to identify an unknown organism is called "keying out" the organism. You compare the creature to the traits listed in the key couplet by couplet, ignoring areas of the key that do not deal with the organism at hand. The only thing that matters is identifying your particular specimen.

The two choices for each couplet are listed under the same letter or number. For example, the first choice in the key at the end of this chapter is couplet "A," which has to do with leaf shape. The first "A," at the very beginning, concerns leaves that are thin and needle-like. If this does not describe the leaf you are working with, you have to skim through the key until you come to the second "A," which describes broader leaves (finding the second choice is made easier by arranging matching letters so that they are indented the same amount). These are the only choices – your leaf has to be one "A" or the other. Once you determine which one it is, you will use only the couplets listed under that "A." In this key, if you choose the first "A" your next decision is between the two "B's;" the second "A" allows you to skip "B" through "J" and go directly to "K." Depending on which "K" matches your specimen your next choice would be either "L" or "Q" and so on.

This brief key is designed to identify some trees commonly found in Illinois and neighboring states. It is somewhat simplified, containing only those genera likely to be encountered in natural settings or as ornamental plantings and omitting more exotic genera. In most cases the genera are not keyed further into species, as this would require a small book in itself. The key is further simplified by focusing primarily on leaf morphology – it is useless for twigs or barren trees. (Keys do exist for trees using characters such as leaf and bud scars. These are useful for identifying deciduous trees in winter.) Virtually all of the gymnosperms are listed in the first section of the key; the rest are angiosperms.

Despite these limitations the key can be used successfully in many situations. You should practice using it on classroom specimens and on trees around campus until you are comfortable with the process of keying out. Hence, no single exercise is listed in this chapter.

BASIC PLANT MORPHOLOGY

In order to be convenient, most keys are based on physical traits that can be examined visually fairly quickly. (It is possible to identify organisms by sophisticated chemical tests such as DNA fingerprinting, but keys are intended to be used more quickly and easily than that.) The study of the external structure of plants is called plant morphology (plant anatomy concerns the internal structure).

One of the more significant characteristics of a plant body is whether it is **herbaceous** or **woody**. Herbaceous plants are generally soft and green; they have trouble surviving winter weather. Plants that only survive one growing season are called **annuals**. Woody plants start out soft and green, but gradually accumulate hard layers of xylem. Woody plants may survive for years and are called **perennials**. These definitions are generalized, but apply to most plants found in temperate climates.

Leaves are photosynthetic organs that grow from stem nodes. Since nodes are also points where the stem may branch, buds are found where the leaves attach to the stem. When a single leaf occurs at each node the leaf arrangement is **alternate**; when two leaves extend opposite each other at each node the arrangement is called **opposite** (a third possibility, of three or more leaves at each node, gives a **whorled** arrangement, but this is rare).

Leaves vary morphologically much more than stems and are useful in identifying plants. **Simple leaves** consist of a broad **blade** attached to the stem by a stalk. In **compound leaves** the blade is divided into several **leaflets**. The points where the leaflets attach to the petiole are not true nodes and never have buds. Compound leaves can be either **pinnately** or **palmately** arranged (see figure 11.2).

Leaves can be highly modified. In some plants, leaves are small and scale-like. Others are pointed like awls or needles. Specially modified leaves can even perform functions other than photosynthesis. Leaves can participate in reproduction, as when they produce spores in a strobilus. The protective **thorns** of cacti are also leaves (thorns on other plants are modified stems). Climbing plants use thin curling leaves called **tendrils** to attach themselves to supports. A few plants (for example, the Venus fly-trap) even have leaves capable of trapping and digesting insects in order to make their own high-nitrogen fertilizer.

Figure 11.1. Leaf arrangements

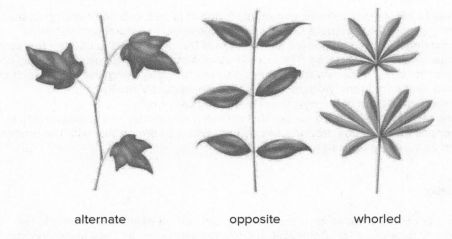

alternate   opposite   whorled

Figure 11.2. Leaf morphology

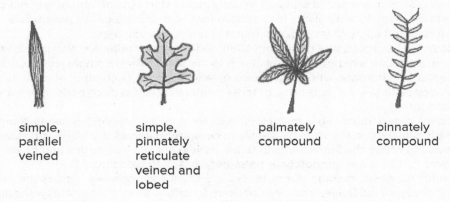

simple,   simple,   palmately   pinnately
parallel   pinnately   compound   compound
veined   reticulate
                 veined and
                 lobed

Important Terms

alternate
annual
blade
compound leaf
dichotomous
herbaceous
key
leaflet
opposite
palmate
perennial
pinnate
simple leaf
tendril
thorn
whorled
woody

KEY TO SELECTED ILLINOIS TREES

A. Leaves narrow, less than 5mm wide, needle-shaped or scale-like

   B. Leaves evergreen, persisting through winter

      C. Leaves in clusters of 2-5, sheathed at the base. . . . . *Pinus* (pines)

      C. Leaves solitary, not clustered

         D. Leaves opposite and scale-like or awl-shaped

            E. Twigs flattened; leaves all of one kind and scale-like; cones about 1 cm long and pale brown. *Thuja occidentalis* (arborvitae)

            E. Twigs essentially circular in cross-section; leaves of two kinds, either awl-shaped or scale-like, often both on same branch; cone berrylike and bluish. . . . . *Juniperus virginiana* (juniper)

         D. Leaves spirally arranged or apparently alternate, needle-like in shape

            F. Leaves square in cross-section (feeling ridged when rolled between fingers). . . . . *Picea* (spruces)

            F. Leaves definitely flattened in cross-section

               G. Twigs remaining green into the summer of the year after they were formed (Note: this refers to the twigs themselves, not just the needles). . . . . *Taxus* (yews)

               G. New twigs turning brown or gray by the autumn of the year in which they form

                  H. Leaves pale green and attached smoothly to twig; cones 2-9 cm long and upright. . . . . *Abies* (firs)

                  H. Leaves darker green and attached to raised bumps on twig surface; cones less than 6 cm long and hanging down from twigs

                     I. Needles with a pair of pale parallel lines underneath; cones less than 4 cm long and without long bracts. . . . *Tsuga canadensis* (Canadian hemlock)

                     I. Needles without pair of lines underneath; cones over 4 cm long with long 3-pointed bracts emerging from beneath cone scale. . . . . *Pseudotsuga meziesii* (Douglas-fir)

   B. Leaves deciduous, falling in autumn, or, when present, appearing only on newly grown twigs

J. Leaves clustered on spur shoots, twigs not deciduous in autumn; cones 1-2 cm long and borne on lateral branches, scales open and attached at base. . . . . *Larix* (larches and tamaracks)

J. Leaves solitary and evenly spaced, whole twigs deciduous in autumn; cones 2-4 cm long and borne terminally, cone scales peltate (attached by central stalk). . . . . *Taxodium distichum* (bald cypress)

A. Leaves more than 5mm wide, not needle-shaped or scale-like

K. Leaves compound, with several leaflets on a single stalk

L. Leaves opposite

M. Leaves palmately compound, with 5 or 7 leaflets; fruit leathery and containing a single large seed ("buckeye"). . . . . *Aesculus* (buckeyes and horse chestnuts)

M. Leaves pinnately compound, with more than 5 leaflets; fruit small and winged. . . . . *Fraxinus* (ashes)

L. Leaves alternate

N. Leaves twice or more compound, leaflets less than 2 cm wide; fruit a brown legume pod. . . . . *Gleditsia triacanthos* (honey locust)

N. Leaves once compound, leaflets more than 2 cm wide; fruit not a pod

O. Plants shrubs or small trees; fruits berrylike and in clusters. . . . . *Rhus* (sumacs and poison ivy)

O. Plants solitary trees, large at maturity; fruit a nut

P. Fruit husk splitting at maturity. . . . . *Carya* (hickories)

P. Fruit husk not split at maturity. . . . . *Juglans* (walnuts)

K. Leaves simple, with a single leaf blade on a leaf stalk

Q. Leaves fanlike, with all veins parallel to each other; leaves borne on short spur shoots. . . . . *Ginkgo biloba* (ginkgo)

Q. Leaves not fanlike, or veins not parallel to each other; leaves not borne on spur shoots

R. Leaves opposite or whorled

S. Leaves whorled, 3 at a node; leaves unlobed; fruit a long slender pod. . . . . . .
. . . . *Catalpa speciosa* (catalpa)

S. Leaves opposite and lobed; fruits winged. . . . . *Acer* (maples)

R. Leaves alternate

T. Leaf margins smooth

U. Leaves unlobed. . . . . *Magnolia* (magnolias)

U. Leaves lobed

V. Leaves pinnately lobed; fruit an acorn. . . . .*Quercus* (oaks)

V. Leaves palmately lobed or star-shaped; fruit not an acorn . . . .
. . . . *Liriodendron tulipfera* (tuliptree)

T. Leaf margins toothed or serrate (saw-like)

X. Flowers borne on catkins

Y. Mature fruits hairy, forming a cottony cluster

Z. Leaves narrow, 1 to 3 cm wide. . . . . *Salix* (willows)

Z. Leaves broad, rounded or triangular, more than 3 cm wide. . . . .
. . . . *Populus* (poplars and aspens)

Y. Mature fruits hard

AA. Bark brown to dark gray, not papery or peeling; fruits tough, woody,
and cone-like. . . . . *Alnus* (alders)

AA. Bark white to yellow-brown, smooth or peeling; fruits a drooping string
of nutlets . . . . *Betula* (birches)

X. Flowers not borne on catkins

BB. Leaves unlobed and asymmetrical with an uneven base

CC. Fruit spherical and maturing in summer. . . . . . . *Tilia* (basswoods)

CC. Fruit flattened and winged, maturing in early spring or fall. . . . .
. . . . *Ulmus* (elms)

BB. Leaves lobed or symmetrical if unlobed

   DD. Leaves lobed

      EE. Leaves with 3 or 5 lobes; fruits tiny and in spherical clusters. . . .
         . . . . *Plantanus* (sycamores)

      EE. Leaves mitten-shaped, fruit berrylike. . . . . . *Morus* (mulberries)

   DD. Leaves unlobed but symmetrical

      FF. Thorns present on at least some branches; seedlike structure
         inside of fruit very hard and bony. . . . *Crataegus* (hawthorns)

      FF. Thorns absent; seeds not contained inside a hardened structure
         within fruit. . . . . *Malus* (apples and crabapples)

CHAPTER 12
THE RISE OF THE
ANIMAL KINGDOM

INTRODUCTION

Fossils and molecular data suggest that the first multicellular organisms were algae which lived between a billion and one and a half billion years ago. As we have seen, it took over 800 million years for these algae to give rise to land plants. In the meantime, animals evolved in the seas. Most kinds of animals still live in the seas today, terrestrial species being common only among the arthropods and chordates (see chapters 13 and 14). Although the connection between animals and protists is not as clear as it is with plants, a fair amount of evidence indicates that animals evolved from a particular kind of flagellated organism, some species of which form simple round colonies that look a little like the alga *Volvox*. By the end of the Cambrian Period (500 million years ago) all major animal phyla had appeared.

The phylogenetic history of the animals is in many ways the easiest to study of any group of organisms. Animals have an extensive fossil record and an incredible array of complex structures that can be studied for homologies. More importantly, animals exhibit a very intricate pattern of development as they grow from a zygote into an adult. The study of an individual organism's development is called **embryology**. Through embryology zoologists have found that many different animal structures can arise from similar embryological tissue and are therefore homologous. In many cases the difference between one type of animal and another is due to a small shift in developmental patterns early in life. Creatures that are virtually identical at one stage of development may end up looking completely different as adults.

TRENDS IN ANIMAL EVOLUTION

All animals are multicellular heterotrophic eukaryotes. Some are parasites on (or in) other animals, but most are **holotrophs,** meaning they eat other organisms and digest their whole tissues to release nutrients. (Carnivores are holotrophs that eat animals, herbivores eat plants, and omnivores will eat almost anything.) The needs of a holotrophic life-style have been the major influences on animal evolution. Animals generally must seek out, capture, and ingest prey. This is facilitated by multicellularity, as the presence of many cells allows for tissue specialization. Animals (except for a few highly specialized parasites) have mouths and digestive systems. Most have muscle cells that permit movement and nerve cells to carry messages quickly from one part of the body to another. Coordinated movement is a great advantage in finding and capturing food.

An animal should have a fairly definite shape if it is to move efficiently. The simplest shape is roundness – being the same in all directions. Since an animal must have a mouth, the perfect symmetry of a sphere is impossible, as the mouth would be on one side only. Thus the simplest shape available to animals is **radial symmetry**: round with a definite top and bottom (like a cylindrical vase with an opening in the top). The simplest animals we shall consider are radially symmetrical.

In order for an animal to be a good predator, it is helpful for it to have a sense of direction. This requires stretching the animal into a **bilaterally symmetrical** shape, one that not only has a top and bottom but also a front and back and left and right. Such shapes can include fins and legs to aid locomotion. Most animals are bilaterally symmetrical.

A bilaterally symmetrical animal will find food more easily if its front end is equipped with eyes or other sense organs. When one end of an animal possesses sense organs and the nervous tissue necessary to interpret the information being sensed (that is, a brain), it has a head and is said to be **cephalized**. Some of the simple animals described below are cephalized, and some are not.

The final trend in animal evolution has to do with the complexity of the body tissues. The mouth leads to the digestive cavity which is the inner surface of the animal. The skin, or **epidermis**, is the outer surface. The simplest animals have only these two layers, with the narrow space between them filled with fluid and perhaps a few cells that are not organized into any definite tissue. In more complex animals this space is completely filled with cells of **mesodermal** tissue. Mesoderm contains muscles, so such animals have greatly improved mobility.

In some animals the mesoderm itself becomes organized into layers. Roundworms have a fluid-filled cavity between their gut and a layer of mesoderm that lines the inside of the skin. This cavity is called a **pseudocoelom** to distinguish it from a true **coelom**, an internal body cavity lined on all sides with mesodermal tissue. Most familiar animals, from earthworms to humans, have a coelom. In a human the coelom is the body cavity between the internal organs and the muscles of the body wall.

Taken together, animal's symmetry, tissue organization, and general structure constitute a **body plan**. Each animal phylum is defined by a particular body plan.

THE BASE OF THE ANIMAL FAMILY TREE

Sponges are the simplest animals but in many respects they are very different from other animals. We will therefore ignore them here. **Cnidarians** (Phylum Cnidaria) are the simplest animals on the main evolutionary line of the animal kingdom. They are radially symmetrical and have bodies made of only two cell layers: the epidermis and the inner **gastrodermis** (in some species a third layer of mesoderm-derived cells lies in between these layers). The gastrodermis lines an internal **gastrovascular cavity** that is open only at the mouth. Food entering the gastrovascular cavity is digested and absorbed by the gastrodermis, which means that cnidarians can ingest food particles larger than single cells. Most cnidarians are active predators, grabbing prey with their many **tentacles** and forcing it into their mouths. In fact, cnidarians get their name from the stinging **cnidocytes** (from the Greek *knide*, nettle, a prickly plant) that are borne on their tentacles. When irritated, cnidocytes eject pointed threads that either inject poison into the prey or wrap around its smaller appendages. Cnidocytes are unique to cnidarians.

Cnidarians are widespread in oceans and to a much lesser extent in freshwater. **Jellyfish** are cnidarians. Another group, the **corals**, is very important ecologically because they build **coral reefs** which serve as habitats for many kinds of animals and algae. Cnidarians engage in various symbiotic relationships, the most important of which occurs when they become infested with photosynthetic algae. While this process can be an important factor in the food chain of a coral reef, it also makes the reef very sensitive to light and other factors that affect algal growth.

Cnidarians exhibit two body types: **polyps** and **medusae** (figure 12.1). Some species exist only as polyps or only as medusae, but most have a life cycle which alternates between the two. An animal life cycle shows how a zygote develops into a larva and then into successive adult shapes. It does <u>not</u> involve alternation of generations.

Figure 12.1. Cnidarian body types

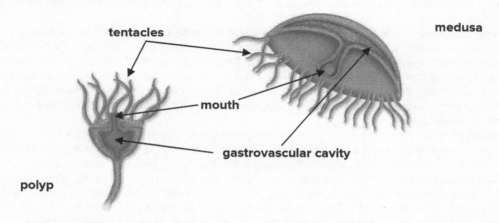

Jellyfish illustrate the cnidarian life cycle well (figure 12.2). As in most animals, the zygote divides mitotically to form a hollow ball called a **blastula**. Continuing mitosis fills the blastula and turns it into a solid larva called a **planula**. Planulae are covered with cilia and are free-swimming. When they find a suitable substrate they attach themselves and begin to grow into a polyp, forming a mouth, gastrovascular cavity, and tentacles. The polyp eventually elongates into a **strobila**, which looks something like a tiny stack of plates. Each of the "plates" breaks off of the strobila and grows into a separate medusa. The medusae from any given strobila are all genetically identical clones. The medusae are the sexually mature adults, producing sperm and eggs that are shed into the gastrovascular cavity from the gonads and exit the animals through the mouth. These fuse into new zygotes to complete the life cycle.

Figure 12.2. Life cycle of the jellyfish *Aurelia*

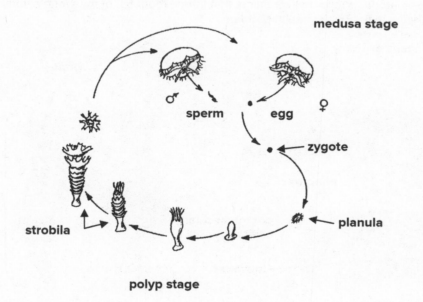

Cnidarians are effective predators and have survived for half a billion years. Nevertheless, they are rather limited by their structural simplicity. The next big step in animal evolution was the development of bilateral symmetry.

It is convenient to be able to refer unambiguously to the different directions of a bilateral body, so the following terms are used by zoologists: **Anterior** refers to the head end of the animal while **posterior** refers to the tail. An animal's belly is on the **ventral** side and the back is **dorsal**. These terms are independent of the way an animal happens to be positioned – for example, the backbones of both dogs and humans are dorsal, even though the dog backbone is horizontal and the human backbone vertical. As the animals we study become more complex, these terms will become increasingly useful in describing the positions of organs and other structures.

Flatworms (Phylum Platyhelminthes) are the simplest bilateral animals. They are small solid creatures that look somewhat like elongated planulae. Most free-living flatworms are much more complex than this, however. They exhibit three well-developed tissue layers and many are cephalized as well.

Like cnidarians, flatworms have a single opening into the gastrovascular cavity. However, the space between the gastrovascular cavity and the epidermis is a solid mass of mesoderm leaving no body cavity between the gut and the body wall. This explains why flatworms are flat: There is no internal fluid to transport material around their bodies, so all of the internal tissues must be close to either the epidermis or the gastrodermis. In many flatworms the gastrovascular cavity is highly branched so that it reaches into all portions of the animal.

Some flatworms are free-living and others are parasitic. The planarians are a group of free-living worms that includes both fresh water and marine species. A few planarians even live in moist soil in tropical environments. Planarians are active predators and scavengers. They are cephalized and have a head with light-sensitive **eyespots** and an organized nervous system (see figure 12.3). They can even be trained to follow simple paths and respond to particular stimuli. The mouth is not on the head – it is at the end of a muscular tube (the pharynx) that extends from the gastrovascular cavity out the "belly" of the worm.

Commonly called **flukes**, **trematodes** are flatworms that are internal parasites of vertebrates. The adults look quite similar to planarians although they lack eyespots and other sense organs which have little value to a life-style spent inside an animal host. Many trematodes have one or two intermediate hosts before they can enter their primary host and become sexually mature. For example, the Chinese liver fluke develops first inside a snail, and then moves on to a fish. Humans contract them from eating raw fish. **Schistosomes** are trematodes similar to liver flukes that infect about 5% of the world's human population. Schistosomiasis is thus a major public health problem.

Figure 12.3. Planaria anatomy

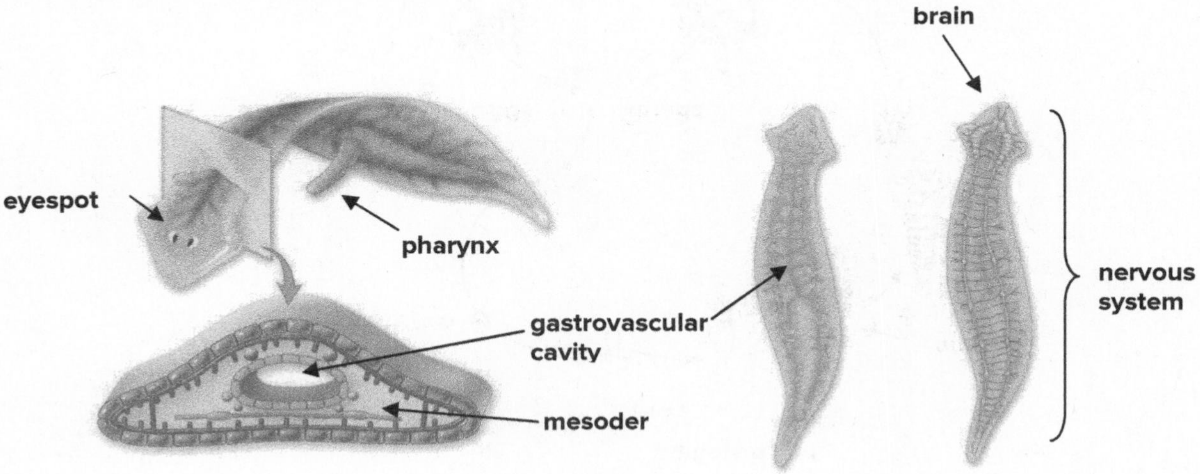

brain

eyespot

pharynx

gastrovascular cavity

mesoder

nervous system

Tapeworms are also parasitic flatworms. They live in the gut of vertebrate hosts. Tapeworms derive nutrients predigested from their host and do not have their own digestive system. A mature tapeworm is structurally similar to a scyphozoan strobila in that it is a long chain of subunits that mature and break off to become independent sexually-reproducing individuals. The worm is anchored to the intestinal wall of its host by a **scolex** (figure 12.4). The scolex is often called the worm's "head" because it is round and located at the end of the worm. However, it is not cephalized in the sense that it has sense organs or a brain — tapeworms have a greatly reduced nervous system. The scolex is equipped with hooks and suckers so it can act as an efficient anchor. Growing from the scolex is a string of **proglottids**. Each proglottid is physiologically and reproductively independent and as such is homologous to an individual fluke or planarian. Most of the proglottid is taken up by reproductive organs. Each one produces copious amounts of eggs that are released as the proglottid matures. Since the tapeworm is an intestinal parasite, the eggs are released in the host's feces. Animals eating contaminated food pick up the eggs and continue the life cycle. For example, eggs of the beef tapeworm are ingested by cows. When the eggs hatch the larvae burrow into the bovine muscle and form cysts. Humans are infected by the cysts when they eat poorly cooked beef.

Figure 12.4. Tapeworm morphology

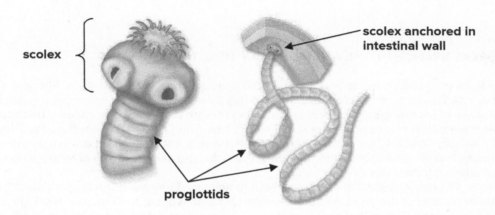

PROTOSTOMES AND DEUTEROSTOMES

In all animals (except sponges) the zygote grows by cell division until it expands into a balloon-like hollow sphere. This hollow embryo is called a blastula. In cnidarians the blastula fills with new cells to become a solid planuloid larva. However, in higher animals, one side of the blastula "caves in", creating a cup-shaped structure two cells thick (figure 12.5). The outer layer of cells is destined to become the skin and the inner layer the gastrovascular cavity, but in an embryo the outer layer is called **ectoderm** and the inner layer **endoderm**. The cup-shaped embryo is a **gastrula**. In flatworms, the gastrula develops into the adult and there is always just a single opening into the gastrovascular cavity. In **protostome** animals a second opening forms in the other side of the gastrula which ultimately becomes the **anus**, creating an efficient, one-way digestive system. ("Protostome" comes from the Greek *protos*, first, and *stoma*, mouth, and refers to the fact that the mouth forms first.)

As development of the protostome embryo continues, cells migrate into the space between the endoderm and ectoderm to form mesoderm. The rest of the internal cavity is filled with fluid. The fluid-filled space is either a pseudocoelom or a true coelom, depending upon how the mesoderm is arranged around the space.

Adult protostomes come in all shapes and sizes from clams to butterflies. Their early development does set patterns, however. All protostomes have ventral nerve cords and hearts or major blood vessels dorsal to the nerve cord. In chapter 14 we shall see that another branch of the animal kingdom, the **deuterostomes**, develops in the opposite fashion.

Figure 12.5. Gastrulation

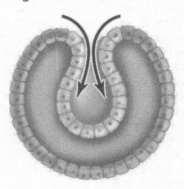

THE FIRST GREAT BRANCH OF THE ANIMAL FAMILY TREE: TROCHOZOANS

The complex body plan of an adult animal develops from the gastrula in several steps. First the anus forms, completing the one-way path of the digestive tract. At this point the embryo is no longer a gastrula but is some kind of larva. In several groups of animals this larva takes a particular form called a **trochophore**. Trochophores have bands of cilia and swim about as tiny free-living creatures while they feed and grow. Depending on exactly how they grow, trochophores can develop into animals as diverse as the various forms of **mollusks** and **annelids**. Or put another way, mollusks and annelids, very different as adults, are related evolutionarily by their similar embryology.

The annelids (Phylum Annelida) are long segmented animals. They are often simply called "segmented worms." Annelids include earthworms and their relatives, marine worms, and leeches. Most are aquatic (both fresh and salt water). Those that are terrestrial are limited to moist habitats, since they are quite susceptible to desiccation. Aquatic annelids include the tubifex worms sold as fish food; other species can be microscopically small.

Earthworms are the most familiar members of the phylum, and illustrate the main features of annelid anatomy well (figure 12.6). Unlike flatworms, segmented worms have a complete digestive system with two openings, a mouth and an anus. Thus their body plan can be thought of as a tube within a tube. We shall see that other animals have bodies that are also built upon a basic tube-within-a-tube plan, but in some cases this body plan is highly modified.

The internal cavity of an earthworm is a true coelom and the body is segmented – that is, it shows a repeating pattern of muscles and other structures divided internally by membranous **septa**. Nevertheless, the segments are not repetitive independent units like the proglottids of a tapeworm. Many organs and organ systems extend through multiple segments and are not repeated. The segments mainly affect locomotion, as the ability to change the shape of each segment independently allows segmented worms to crawl across a surface. This is facilitated by the presence of short bristles on the surface of each segment that provide traction.

Figure 12.6. Earthworm anatomy

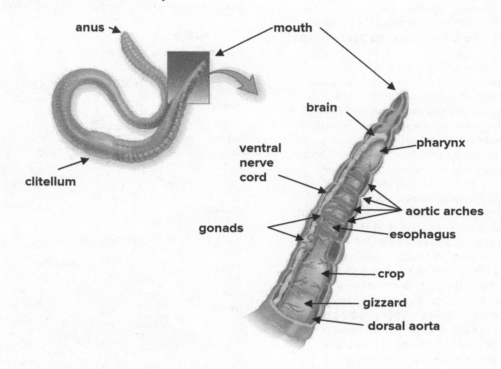

anus

mouth

clitellum

brain

ventral nerve cord

pharynx

gonads

aortic arches

esophagus

crop

gizzard

dorsal aorta

Most of the organs are located in the anterior segments. Here there is considerable differentiation of the digestive system. A muscular **pharynx** helps to draw food into the mouth and push it through the **esophagus** to an enlarged storage organ, the **crop**. The crop slowly releases the food to the **gizzard**, which is heavily muscled and grinds the food by mixing it with grit and sand ingested as the worm eats. The resulting mash passes into the long **intestine** that extends through most of the worm. Here enzymes digest the food into small molecules that can be absorbed into the blood. A large **dorsal aorta** runs down the back of the digestive tract and moves blood past the intestine continuously. A second blood vessel runs ventral to the digestive tract and is connected to the dorsal aorta by five **aortic arches** in the esophageal region. These arches are muscular and pump blood through the vessels like hearts. In worms the blood is always kept separate from the coelomic fluid. As in all protostomes, the **nerve cord** is ventral to the digestive system and aortas.

Also in the anterior segments are the **gonads** and associated reproductive structures. Earthworms are bisexual, or **hermaphroditic**, so each produces both sperm and eggs. When two worms mate, they touch ventral surfaces, aligning their genital pores. The large anterior segment, or **clitellum**, secretes a sticky mucus that holds the worms together as each delivers sperm to the other's seminal receptacle. Some time after the worms separate the clitellum secretes a sheath of mucus and chitin that slides over the head of the worm, collecting eggs and the partner's sperm in the process. The sheath holds the sperm and eggs together in a moist **cocoon**. Here fertilization actually takes place. The cocoon protects the embryos until the eggs hatch into tiny worms (earthworms do not go through a trochophore larva stage as marine annelids do).

Marine worms are generally much more complex than earthworms. They have well-developed heads with sense organs and often tentacles. Some are "tube worms" that hide most of their bodies inside a buried tube, only extending their tentacles and gills. All that is usually visible of such animals is a very unworm-like display of feathery appendages, a display that can be beautifully colorful.

Leeches are quite similar to earthworms except that they have suckers at one or both ends of their bodies. They do not have septa inside their bodies, so only their body walls are segmented. This alters their locomotion somewhat, and leeches use their suckers extensively when they move. Only a few species of leeches suck blood from other animals — most prey on small worms or scavenge dead animals.

Mollusks (Phylum Mollusca) are quite different in appearance from annelids: they are fleshy animals that usually have shells. The phylum is large, containing well over 100,000 species of chitons, clams, snails, slugs, squids and octopuses. Most are aquatic, but some snails and slugs live in moist terrestrial habitats. Clams, snails, and squids may not seem to have very much in common, but careful study reveals that all of them have the same basic body plan, consisting of three main regions: a muscular **foot**, a **visceral mass** (containing the digestive, circulatory, excretory, and reproductive organs), and, covering the visceral mass, a soft **mantle**. The mantle is a distinctive mollusk structure. It wraps around the main body of the animal, shrouding it inside a protective mantle cavity. Inside the mantle cavity lies a specialized portion of the mantle, the **gills**. The gills are covered with beating cilia that create a constant current of water through the mantle cavity, the water entering and exiting the mantle cavity through tubular extensions of the mantle called **siphons**. As the water passes over the gills oxygen diffuses into the gill tissue and enters the animal's blood. In most mollusks the mantle also secretes a calcareous shell. Figure 12.7 illustrates how all of these regions can be seen in different mollusks when they are similarly aligned.

Most of the body regions can be seen easily in chitons, which are similar to the more familiar snails and slugs (**gastropods**). Chitons have shells made of eight plates while gastropods have one-piece shells. (A few gastropods, such as slugs and marine nudibranchs, have no shells but retain the basic gastropod body plan.) The only terrestrial mollusks are gastropods, and there are several thousand species of these. At least two thirds of gastropod species are aquatic, however, most being marine.

Gastropods use their foot to crawl around in search of food. The anterior portion of the foot is cephalized. The mouth is located in the head, as are sensory tentacles, which often have eyes at their tips. Inside the mouth is a **radula**, a hard, toothed tongue common in many mollusks. Herbivorous gastropods use their radulas to scrape algae from rocks while carnivorous

species use them to bore through the shells of prey and tear off bits of flesh into their mouths.

Figure 12.7. The mollusk body plan.

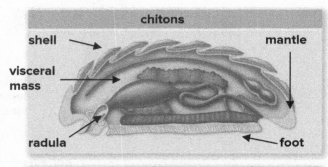

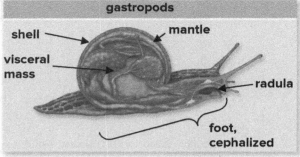

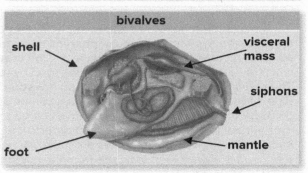

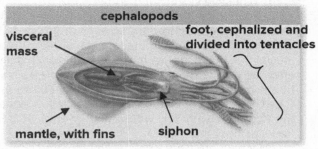

Oysters, clams, mussels, and scallops are all **bivalves**. The name refers to the two-part shell that is hinged along the animal's dorsal midline. Notice that this means that the "top" of a clam is the shell hinge and the "bottom" is the foot – most people are accustomed to seeing bivalves in the grocery store where they are displayed lying on their sides. Bivalves are sedentary creatures that "filter-feed" by straining bacteria, protists, and minute invertebrates from the water passing through their mantles. They generally use their feet to dig themselves into soft sand, opening their shells just enough to extend their siphons.

Cephalopods are the largest and behaviorally most complex of all invertebrates. The word "cephalopod" comes from the Greek *kephale*, head, and *podos*, foot, indicating that the foot region of these animals is, paradoxically, highly cephalized, exhibiting large eyes and a well-developed brain. The edge of the foot is subdivided into grasping tentacles equipped with suction cups or hooks. Octopuses have eight such tentacles, squids ten, and nautiluses dozens. Fish or other prey (cephalopods are all carnivorous) seized by the tentacles are torn apart by the animal's beak-like jaws and radula.

Ancient fossil cephalopods have shells but shells are reduced or absent in most modern species. Octopuses have no shell and are very soft and flexible. Squids have a small flat shell under the mantle which helps to stiffen the animal in a pointy, aerodynamic shape that makes for speedy swimming. Only nautiluses have shells similar to those of other mollusks. These are spiral and develop internal chambers as the animal grows. All cephalopods circulate water through their mantle cavities like other mollusks do. They have the unique ability to force water out of their siphons under pressure as a means of "jet propulsion" and so are very fast.

THE SECOND GREAT BRANCH OF THE ANIMAL FAMILY TREE: ECDYSOZOANS

Not all protostomes go through a trochophore larval stage. Another group of protostome animals, in fact, the largest group of animals, develops in a very different way, involving the repeated **molting** of a tough, external **cuticle**. As with the trochozoans, this pattern of molting leads to two rather different-looking phyla of animals. These are the **roundworms** (Phylum Nematoda) and **arthropods** (Phylum Arthropoda). The arthropods are an enormous phylum, with four times as many species as even the flowering plants. As a result, their story will spill over into chapter 13.

Figure 12.8. Anatomy of the roundworm *Ascaris*

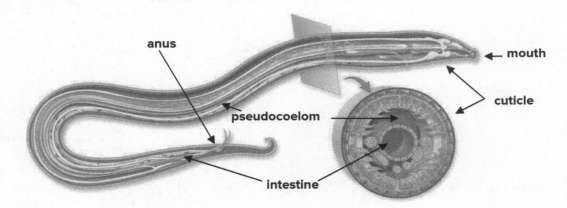

There are about 25,000 known species of roundworms, but zoologists estimate there may be over ten times as many yet to be discovered. There are both parasitic and free-living species, the latter being found in all kinds of aquatic or moist habitats. They are so plentiful in the soil that it is said that if the entire rest of the earth were to suddenly disappear, there would be enough remaining nematodes to allow you to recognize the continents from outer space.

Nematodes have internal organs suspended in a fluid-filled pseudocoelom. The layer of longitudinal muscles just under the skin makes roundworms capable of a thrashing wriggling motion not seen in other worms. Roundworm anatomy is illustrated in figure 12.8. Note that nematode structure is roughly similar to that of an earthworm: it is a long tube within a tube. However there is no segmentation and the anatomy is a bit simpler. The size range of nematodes is also similar to that of annelids: a few millimeters to several centimeters.

Roundworms parasitize numerous plants and animals. Humans are affected by hookworms, intestinal roundworms (*Ascaris*), and *Trichinella*, among other nematodes. Heartworm in dogs is also caused by roundworms. On the other hand, non-parasitic roundworms, especially the species *Caenorhabditis elegans*, have become very valuable for experiments on animal development.

Arthropods are far more complex than roundworms. Their cuticle is developed into a chitinous **exoskeleton**. The thickness and rigidity of the exoskeleton vary from species to species and even from place to place on the same animal (the softer areas are necessary for flexibility). Like annelids, all arthropods have a segmented body plan. However, arthropods have a pair of jointed appendages on each segment (the name Arthropoda is derived from the Greek *arthron*, joint, and *podos*, foot). Individual segments and their appendages can be highly modified. A feature common among arthropods is that segments are arranged and even fused into specialized regions, or **tagmata**. The bodies of some arthropods (for example, spiders) show so much fusion that segmentation can be difficult to see. Since the basic arthropod body plan has a pair of appendages on each segment, it is sometimes possible to infer how many segments are fused into a single tagma by counting the appendages it has.

Fossils indicate that arthropods are an extremely old group. Among the extinct arthropods are the famous **trilobites**, which were very common hundreds of millions of years ago. The segmentation in trilobites was obvious and each segment was similar to the next. Other fossil arthropods show the beginnings of specialization in segments and appendages that allow zoologists to group them with the highly modified modern forms that descended from them.

The adaptability of the arthropod body plan is such that it has diversified into at least 1.5 million known species. Every year taxonomists discover thousands of new arthropods, and some speculate that if all of the available habitats were thoroughly searched, another 5,000,000 species would be found. Because of this, the phylum is divided into three subphyla. Two of these are terrestrial and will be examined in the following chapter. Here we will focus on the generally aquatic **crustaceans**.

Figure 12.9. Crayfish morphology

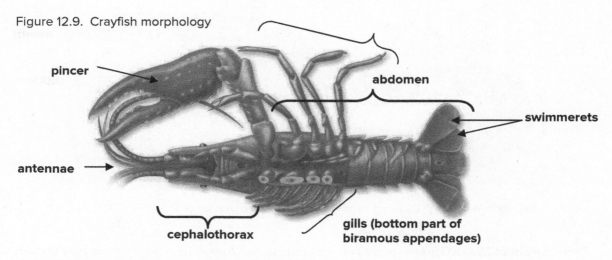

pincer

abdomen

swimmerets

antennae

cephalothorax

gills (bottom part of biramous appendages)

Crustaceans are grouped apart from other arthropods because of their double-branched, or **biramous** appendages. Biramous appendages are often highly modified, but they can be seen plainly in many fossil crustaceans. Typically, the upper branch functions as a **gill** and the lower branch is used for locomotion.

Lobsters, crayfish, crabs, sowbugs, and barnacles are all crustaceans. Numerous species of crustaceans are microscopic and are an important food source for filter feeding animals. Crustaceans are characterized by two body regions, each consisting of several fused segments; the anterior region is the **cephalothorax** and the posterior is the **abdomen.** The number of pairs of segmental appendages varies from species to species. Typically, crustaceans have a pair of jaw-like **mandibles,** two pair of sensory **antennae,** and **compound eyes** made of many facets. The cephalothorax has pairs of long **walking legs,** while the abdominal segments may have small **swimmerets** or other appendages. In some crustaceans large pincers appear on the cephalothorax.

Internally, crustaceans such as crayfish are similar to earthworms. The powerful mandibles are very efficient at chewing food and pushing it into the mouth, so neither pharynx nor gizzards are necessary in these animals. The esophagus leads directly from the mouth to the **stomach,** where digestion begins. The stomach passes food onto the intestine, which runs through all of the posterior segments just as it does in worms. Dorsal to the digestive tract is an aorta with a single heart. In crustaceans the circulatory system is not completely enclosed in vessels as it is in worms. The aorta delivers blood to large open spaces in the body and to the gills that are part of the biramous walking legs. A ventral nerve cord runs through all of the segments.

INVESTIGATIONS WITH SIMPLE ANIMALS

In the exercises below you will deal with both preserved and living animals. Take care with the live creatures — they are small and delicate. They require cool moist surroundings, so do not expose them to any more light than is necessary for your observations and never let them dry out. You should be able to see them move and explore their environment as they search for food. You may even be able to see them eat.

You will also dissect some fairly complex animals. When dissecting, work slowly and carefully. Once a structure is cut apart, it cannot be put back together again! Use forceps to manipulate the structures and expose deeper tissues, cutting only when necessary. Sometimes it will be necessary to use a scalpel to cut into a surface, other times it will be easier to cut with scissors. When cutting, you will find your movements easier to control if you cut away from you while resting your elbows on the table. Use pins to probe small areas and to pin open incisions. When pinning your specimen to your tray, position it near one edge of the tray so that you can view it under the objective of a dissecting microscope. The microscope will be crucial for seeing details.

Investigation #1   Cnidarian structure and behavior

1.   **Living polyps:** Place some living hydra in a deep well slide. These are freshwater cnidarians that exist only as polyps. Observe their motion and how they can change their body shape. Hydra have no organized nervous or muscular systems. Is this reflected in their behavior? Depending on availability, some of the hydra may have green algae growing symbiotically in their tissues. Try to find some of these specimens.
2.   **Jellyfish life cycles:** Preserved specimens of jellyfish are available for your inspection. Examine the slides of scyphozoan planulae, polyps (also called scyphistomas), strobilae, and medusa (ephyrae).

Investigation #2 Survey of flatworm diversity

1. **Planarian morphology and behavior**: Examine a prepared slide of a planaria and locate the gastrovascular cavity and pharynx. Place a living planaria in a deep well slide. Do you see a head with eyespots? When it moves, what direction does it go? How does it respond to light? With high enough magnification you may be able to see the beating cilia on the surface of its body.

2. **Parasites**: Some flukes and tapeworms are on display. How do they compare to a planaria?

Investigation #3 Annelid structure

1. **Trochophore morphology**: Examine a prepared slide of a trochophore from a marine worm. It will look quite simple. See if you can find the bands of cilia on its body. Can you trace the path of its digestive system?

2. **Earthworm dissection**: Obtain a preserved earthworm from your lab instructor. Before pinning it down, look at some of the external features. Can you see the mouth, anus, and clitellum? Rub your finger along the ventral surface and feel the bristles. Put the worm, ventral side down, in your dissecting pan and pin down the head and tail.

   Make an incision down the dorsal surface, taking care not to cut too deep. Carefully run a pin along the inside of the skin on each side of the incision to destroy the internal septa – this will make it much easier to open the incision and expose the viscera. Use pins to keep the incision open. The gonads and associated structures should be visible as small whitish particles packed along the digestive tract in the anterior segments. Gently push them aside with a pin. Starting at the mouth, locate the major sections of the digestive system. Locate the dorsal aorta and follow it forward to the aortic arches. Move the intestine aside and look for the ventral nerve cord. If you have been extremely careful, you may have preserved the tiny brain anterior to the pharynx. Look for it under the dissecting microscope.

Investigation #4 Mollusk structure and function

1. **Mollusk diversity**: Several preserved mollusks are on display. Look for evidence of the basic mollusk body plan in these animals.

2. **Radula structure**: One structure most mollusks have is a radula. Examine one on a prepared slide and note the rasping teeth along its edges. See if you can find some live snails grazing algae in the aquarium tank. Watch how they use their radulas to scrape the algae into their mouths.

Investigation #5 Nematode structure and behavior

1. **Nematode movement**: Vinegar eels are nematodes that live in apple cider vinegar. Observe the motion of some living vinegar eels. How does this compare to planaria?

2. **Nematode dissection**: Observe the dissected ascaris. Because of the pseudocoelom, it should open up to reveal an intestine and reproductive organs suspended in an internal cavity. Trace the digestive system and observe the tube-within-a-tube body plan.

Investigation #6 Crustacean structure

1. **Crayfish appendages**: Study the external structures of a preserved crayfish. Appendages are apparent on every segment. How many segments are in the abdomen? The segments of the cephalothorax have fused, but you can still count how many segments make up this region by counting the pairs of attached appendages; how many are there? (Don't forget to count the mouthparts and antennae!)

Starting at the posterior end, carefully remove the appendages from one side of the animal and lay them out on a piece of paper – do not forget the mouth parts or the flattened appendages that look like tail fins. Remember that the gills are part of the walking legs, but do not be surprised if they do not come off with the leg – the attachment is weak. The typical walking leg of a mandibulate arthropod has five sections: the coxa, trochanter, femur, tibia, and tarsus. Which of the crayfish appendages retain these five parts? Note that on the cheliped the "thumb" is actually the tarsus (the most distal section) and the "hand" is simply the tibia (the next to last section) with an extension off to the side.

2. **Crayfish anatomy**:   The cephalothorax of the crayfish is covered by an extension of the exoskeleton called the carapace. After you have removed the appendages from one side, clip away the carapace on the other side to reveal the gills. There should be one feathery gill at the origin of each walking leg. How would this arrangement facilitate respiration? Cut down the dorsal midline of the carapace so you can remove the entire side. Use forceps to remove the muscle that is exposed, taking care not to damage the underlying structures. Cut through the skeletal plates of the abdomen, removing muscle as you go. When the viscera are exposed, trace the path of the digestive system.

3. **Crustacean diversity**: Survey the other crustaceans on display, comparing them to the crayfish you dissected. Pay careful attention to the microscopic animals. You can identify these tiny creatures as arthropods by their exoskeleton and jointed appendages.

Important Terms

abdomen
annelid
antenna
anterior
anus
aortic arch
arthropod
bilateral symmetry
biramous
bivalve
body plan
blastula
cephalization
cephalopod
cephalothorax
clitellum
cnidarian
cnidocyte
cocoon
coelom
compound eye
coral
coral reef
crop
crustacean
cuticle
deuterostome
dorsal
dorsal aorta
ectoderm
embryology
endoderm
epidermis

esophagus
exoskeleton
eyespot
flatworm
fluke
foot
gastrodermis
gastropod
gastrovascular cavity
gastrula
gill
gizzard
gonad
hermaphroditic
holotroph
intestine
jellyfish
leech
mandible
mantle
medusa
mesoderm
mollusk
molt
nerve cord
pharynx
planula
polyp
posterior
proglottid
protostome
pseudocoelom
radial symmetry
radula
roundworm
schistostome
scolex
septum
siphon
stomach
strobila
swimmeret
tagma
tapeworm
tentacle
trematode
trilobite
trochophore
ventral
visceral mass
walking leg

CHAPTER 13
TERRESTRIAL ARTHROPODS

INTRODUCTION

Unlike plants, all animal phyla are essentially aquatic. Although many individual species have come and gone, there have been no new animal phyla (which is to say, no new types of body plans) arising in the past 500 million years. All animals alive today are still variations on the basic body plans that existed in the oceans at the end of the Cambrian Period.

Between 400 and 500 million years ago land plants arose from the charophyte green algae, for the first time creating a food source on dry land. Animals began to follow. As we have seen, a few invertebrates like snails and earthworms are able to survive out of the water as long as they can stay moist. But to become fully adapted to land, animals had to solve the same problems of desiccation, structural support, and reproduction that plants faced. Only two phyla of animals have been able to meet these challenges. The first to do so was the arthropods.

It was the combination of the exoskeleton and adaptable jointed appendages that allowed arthropods to leave the water. The exoskeleton offers strong support and seals moisture inside the arthropod body, while the various appendages permit locomotion and other activity. There are a few terrestrial species of crustaceans, but most terrestrial arthropods are either **chelicerates** or **insects**.

CHELICERATES

In chelicerates the most anterior appendages are modified into mouthparts called **chelicerae**. This feature sets them apart from other arthropods whose first appendages are antennae and whose mouthparts are mandibles. In chelicerates it is the second pair of appendages that are used as "feelers," but they are not antennae. The second appendages can take many forms, such as the pedipalps of spiders or the large pincers of scorpions. For this reason it appears that chelicerates diverged from other arthropods before the various segmental appendages began to specialize. In modern chelicerates the chelicerae are usually specialized into fangs or small pincers.

Among modern chelicerates the horseshoe crabs (which are not really crabs at all) are reasonably similar to the early forms. The most common chelicerates today are all **arachnids**: spiders, mites, scorpions, and "daddy longlegs." Like crustaceans, arachnids are characterized by two body regions, each consisting of several fused segments; the anterior **cephalothorax** and posterior **abdomen.** The cephalothorax has four pairs of **walking legs,** a pair of pedipalps, and a pair of chelicerae. Simple eyes are located on the dorsal surface of this region. In most arachnids the abdominal segments are fused into a unified globular region, but in scorpions it retains its segmented character. There are no segmental appendages on the abdomens of arachnids – they have apparently been lost over millions of years of evolution – but the anatomy of the unusual **book lungs** of chelicerates suggests that they are derived from fused gill-like appendages.

INSECTS

Insects are similar to crustaceans in having mandibles and compound eyes. Most also have simple eyes. Unlike crustaceans insect appendages are always unbranched. Insects are essentially terrestrial; some are aquatic or semi-aquatic but this appears to be a secondary adaptation from terrestrial ancestors.

Included among the insects are the grasshoppers, cockroaches, butterflies, wasps, bees, bugs, beetles, flies, gnats, and a myriad other small crawly things. Insects have three distinct body regions: the **head, thorax,** and **abdomen** (figure 13.1). The head has four pairs of segmental appendages: three are mouthparts (this includes the pair of mandibles) and one is a pair of antennae. On the thorax are three pairs of walking legs. Many insects also have two pairs of **wings** on their thoraxes, but these are not derived from segmental appendages – they are outgrowths of the exoskeleton. In some species stingers or egg-laying tubes, which are formed from appendages, occur on the abdomen. Otherwise the abdomen is free of appendages, as it is in chelicerates.

Figure 13.1. Insect morphology and anatomy

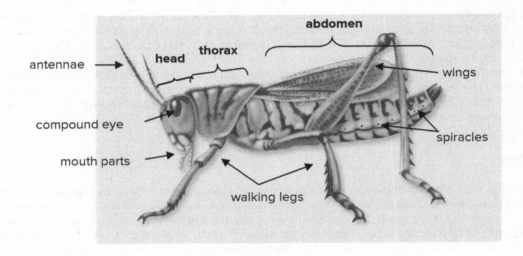

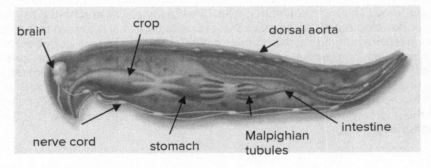

Internally an insect is much like a crayfish except that the digestive tract is slightly modified and there are some adaptations to prevent the insect from drying out. The esophagus expands into a **crop**, which leads to the **stomach**. Tiny threads called **Malpighian tubules** lead into the intestine from the body cavity. These filter waste materials from the body fluids (like a human kidney) and draw them into the intestine so they can be excreted through the anus with any undigested food. This means that insects do not have to waste water by making urine. Another way insects conserve water is through their unique system of **trachea** (figure 13.2), microscopic ducts which carry air throughout the animal's body. Air enters the trachea through valves in the sides of the abdomen called **spiracles**. By closing the spiracles between respiratory movements, insects keep moisture sealed inside their bodies.

On hatching from its egg a young insect may look like a tiny version of an adult of its species, in which case it is called a nymph, or it may be a wormlike larva. Nymphs grow by stages into adults, periodically molting and shedding their outgrown exoskeletons so that they can grow larger. This process is called simple or **incomplete metamorphosis**. The majority of insect species develop by **complete metamorphosis**. In this process, the larval caterpillars, grubs, or maggots molt into successively larger larvae. At a particular point in the life cycle the mature larva turns into a **pupa**. The pupa is an immobile "resting stage" during which the insect radically changes its form. Inside the pupa case, which is either the exoskeleton of the larva or a specially made cocoon, most of the larva's tissues are digested into a gel from which the adult body grows. This is the time when novel structures such as wings and specialized tagmata arise.

Figure 13.2. Insect trachea

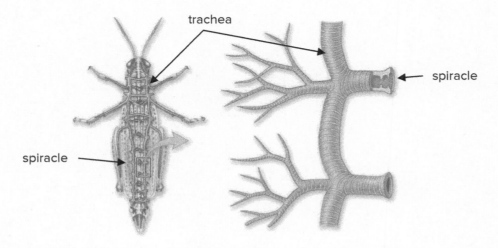

INVESTIGATIONS WITH ARTHROPODS

Investigation #1 Chelicerate structure and diversity
1. **Horseshoe crabs**: Examine a preserved horseshoe crab. How does it compare to the crustaceans you saw last week? Are there antennae? Can you see the chelicerae?
2. **Arachnid diversity**: Survey the different arachnids on display. Compare them to the horseshoe crab.

Investigation #2 Insect structure and function
1. **Insect life cycle**: Observe the displays of metamorphosis. Look for the larvae. How do they compare to adult annelids? How do they compare to the adult insects?
2. **Insect diversity**: Survey the different insects on display. Note how their appendages, including their mouthparts, are modified for different lifestyles. Compare them to the arachnids on display. How can you tell the difference between an insect and an arachnid?

Important Terms

abdomen
arachnid
book lung
cephalothorax
chelicerae
chelicerate
complete metamorphosis
crop
head
incomplete metamorphosis
insect
Malpighian tubule
pupa
spiracle
stomach
thorax
trachea
walking leg
wing

CHAPTER 14
DEUTEROSTOMES

INTRODUCTION

In chapter 12 we described how most animals (protostomes) develop from a blastula into a larva with a complete, one-way digestive tract. Certain groups of animals follow a different developmental pattern. These animals are called deterostomes. There are only two major deuterostome phyla (three phyla of strange marine worms may or may not be related to deuterostomes, but are mainly of interest to specialists anyway). These phyla, the **echinoderms** and **chordates**, are both diverse groups that are very different from each other. However, as deuterostomes, their embryos follow the same plan of development. Therefore all deuterostomes are considered to have originated from a single evolutionary line.

Deuterostomes develop from zygotes in a manner analogous to that of other animals – they form a blastula and then a gastrula (however, the pattern in which the cells divide is slightly different from that of protostomes or flatworms). In deuterostomes a second opening forms in the gastrula just as it does in protostomes, but subsequent development is upside-down relative to protostomes: the original opening into the gastrovascular cavity becomes the anus and the second opening becomes the mouth ("deuterostome" is derived from the Greek for "second mouth"). Protostome and deuterostome embryos also differ in how the coelom develops within the mesoderm (schizocoely versus enterocoely). Deuterostome development is so unique that it seems they branched off from the rest of the animal kingdom's line of evolution at a relatively early stage.

Once the coelom forms, echinoderms and chordates diverge drastically. They do not even have identical larval forms like mollusks and annelids do. The early embryology is really the only thing that echinoderms and chordates have in common. Deuterostome embryology has been studied extensively by biologists because of the insight it presents on human development.

ECHINODERMS

All echinoderms (Phylum Echinodermata) are radially symmetrical, but this is a <u>derived</u> symmetry. In their early stages, echinoderm embryos (and, presumably, their phylogenetic ancestors) are bilaterally symmetrical. Early in life the free-swimming larvae of echinoderms undergo a complex metamorphosis to become radially symmetrical adults.

The bodies of adult echinoderms are often rough and hard. Most echinoderms have an endoskeleton of calcareous plates under a thin skin. Some also have long spines mounted in the endoskeleton. The echinoderm body plan is very unusual because it is based on a five-fold symmetry, as exemplified by the familiar five-armed sea stars. Many echinoderms are sedentary, but the sea stars are relatively active predators and play an important role in the ecology of ocean reefs, where they feed on corals and the bivalves that are often attached to them. Sea urchins and sand dollars are also echinoderms. Neither urchins nor sand dollars have arms, but their internal anatomy is still arranged in five parts. Sea urchins and sea stars are both used by biologists for studies of embryology.

CHORDATES

Although Phylum Chordata does not contain as many species as Arthropoda or Mollusca, it does include the largest and structurally most complex animals on earth: the **vertebrates**. Humans, and, in fact, most familiar animals, are all vertebrates.

The reason chordates are able to become so large and complex has to do once again with embryology. The dorsal ectoderm of a chordate gastrula sinks slightly to form what is called a **neural groove** (figure 14.1). The edges of ectoderm on each side of the neural groove fold up and inward, finally forming a hollow **neural tube.** The neural tube gives rise to the nervous system, which even in the most advanced vertebrates is still based on a hollow nerve cord running along the back of the animal – the spinal cord. (Notice that the nervous system originates from the same embryological tissue as the skin – not the mesoderm!) The tissue just below the neural tube hardens into a firm rod called the **notochord.** In simple chordates the notochord acts like a skeleton, but in vertebrates it becomes incorporated into a rigid and sturdy bony skeletal system. Unlike the exoskeleton of arthropods, the internal skeleton of vertebrates is made of living tissue which grows along with the rest of the animal.

Figure 14.1. Neural tube formation

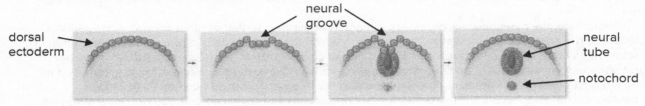

dorsal ectoderm

neural groove

neural tube

notochord

After the neural tube begins to form in the chordate embryo, the internal tissues become segmented like those of annelids and arthropods. The segmentation is not obvious in most mature chordates (just as segments often fuse in adult arthropods) but a few traces usually remain. In vertebrates the rows of bones in the vertebral column and rib cage are vestiges of this segmentation.

In addition to the notochord and hollow dorsal nerve cord, all chordates exhibit two other features during at least part of their lives: rows of **pharyngeal slits** (another segmented characteristic) and a **post-anal tail**. The pharyngeal slits are used for filter-feeding in some chordates but have become modified for other uses in vertebrates. The tail is distinct from the abdomen in chordates because their digestive tracts do not extend for the entire length of their bodies as do those of worms and arthropods.

The best-known chordates are vertebrates, but there are several types of invertebrate chordates. These animals show all of the traits of chordates (hollow nerve cord, notochord, segmentation, pharyngeal slits, and tail) but their notochord never develops into a vertebral column. Of these, **cephalochordates** display the chordate characteristics most clearly. Commonly called lancelets because of their blade-like shape, these are small sea creatures, something between a worm and a tiny fish (figure 14.2)

Figure 14.2. Cephalochordate anatomy

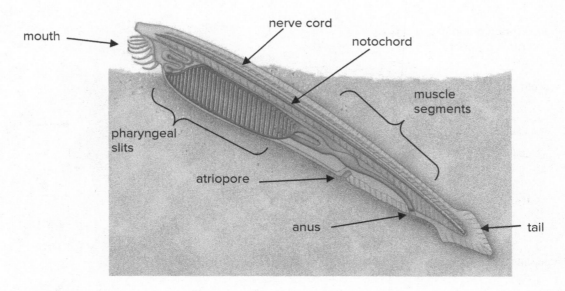

Although lancelets are reasonably good swimmers, they are not very active and tend to bury themselves with just their mouths extending above the sand. They are filter-feeders similar to clams, in this case drawing water into their mouths, straining it through their pharyngeal slits, and expelling it through an opening called an atriopore. Cephalochordates bear a fair resemblance to the earliest chordates in the fossil record.

VERTEBRATES

Vertebrates are animals in which the notochord has given way to a segmented **vertebral column**, or backbone. The oldest fossils of vertebrates are of fish covered in bony plates but lacking jaws. The only jawless vertebrates living today are the lampreys and hagfishes. These animals have no appendages and look a little like large lancelets. However, modern lampreys and hagfishes have relatively soft skeletons made of cartilage instead of bony plates and are thus highly modified from the primitive jawless fishes. Sharks and their relatives also have cartilaginous skeletons but probably evolved from ancestors with bony skeletons, in this case the ancient armored fishes. The armored fishes were the first vertebrates with **jaws**.

The pharynxes of cartilaginous fishes shed light on the origin of jaws. They have rows of slits in them like the filter-feeding chordates, but the framework between the slits has been hardened by cartilage and the whole structure serves as a solid framework for the gills. That is, they have become a series of **gill arches**. Examination of the jaws of cartilaginous fishes indicates that they are simply the most anterior gill arches in modified form. Once jaws evolved they greatly enhanced the ability of vertebrates to hunt and feed, and the fossil record indicates that they diversified rapidly, giving rise to the bony fishes.

The bony fishes are the most numerous vertebrates, both in terms of individuals and species (about 30,000). Although vertebrates underwent many modifications when they adapted to terrestrial life, we can still use a typical fish to illustrate vertebrate anatomy.

Figure 14.3. Fish anatomy

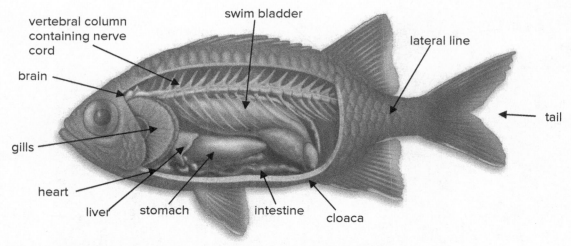

Fish are shaped similarly to lancelets but are more muscular and mobile and have many more specialized structures. The fish's ability to swim comes from the numerous fins, which in modern fish are not supported by many bones (terrestrial vertebrates evolved from primitive fish with bony lobed fins). Each side of the fish is equipped with a **lateral line system.** This is a sense organ made of a series of pores. Vibrations and changes in water pressure are detected by the lateral line system. On either side of the head is a flap of skin called the **operculum.** By moving the operculum back and forth, a fish maintains a steady stream of water across its gills. Sharks, which lack opercula, must swim almost constantly in order to keep water moving through their gills, and can only rest in water with a strong and steady current.

Behind the gills is the **liver**, a complex organ which helps maintain the internal body chemistry of the animal. It also produces digestive enzymes for the **stomach.** The stomach leads to a winding **intestine**, which ends at the **cloaca**, the combination anus and urogenital opening. A balloon-like **swim bladder** runs dorsal and parallel to the digestive tract. It is an outgrowth of the pharynx but has nothing to do with digestion – it makes the fish buoyant so it will not sink. Anterior to the stomach and below the liver is the **heart**. It pumps blood to the gills to pick up oxygen and then on to the rest of the body. The circulatory systems of vertebrates are completely enclosed in blood vessels like those of earthworms.

The anterior end of the nerve cord is enlarged into a well-developed **brain.** A vertebrate brain is made of several lobes and is more elaborate than most invertebrate brains.

VERTEBRATE ADAPTATIONS TO TERRESTRIAL ENVIRONMENTS

The majority of vertebrate species are found in the seas as the various kinds of bony fishes. There are only about 25,000 kinds of terrestrial vertebrates, far less than the number of insect species, less even than the number of species of terrestrial gastropods. Still, these animals are what we always think of when we hear the word "animal." Partly this is just prejudice – after all, humans are terrestrial vertebrates. These animals are similar to us and familiar, since they share our dry habitats. We are also attracted to our fellow vertebrates because of their diversity and structural complexity.

Like insects, vertebrates had to overcome the problem of water loss before they could successfully adapt to terrestrial life. The transition was first made by **amphibians**, which are able to function on land but are usually limited to moist environments. Many adult amphibians (e.g., frogs) have **lungs** that provide a moist internal surface for gas exchange (oxygen can only be absorbed through moist membranes). Lungs are an outgrowth of the pharynx homologous to the swim bladders of fish. Even in the most modern vertebrates the access to the lungs is through the pharynx, which is why people can choke if they try to inhale and eat at the same time.

Pumping blood through lungs or gills is hard work. In fish blood flow is sluggish. Terrestrial vertebrates have developed systems of **double circulation** that direct blood to the lungs and then return it to the heart so that the oxygenated blood can be repumped to the rest of the body. Amphibian hearts are not as efficient as those of birds and mammals, but are still an improvement over the one-way circulation in fishes.

The lungs of amphibians are small and inefficient balloons — most of their gas exchange occurs through their thin, moist skin, just as it does in earthworms and snails. Moreover, amphibian eggs are highly susceptible to desiccation and are always laid and hatch in water. Even those amphibians that do breathe air usually have aquatic larvae, for example, the tadpoles of frogs. Thus, despite some adaptations for living on land, amphibians are always tied to water for at least part of their lives.

Amniotes were the first fully terrestrial vertebrates. They appear in the fossil record about 300 million years ago and gradually replaced amphibians as the dominant terrestrial vertebrates.

Amniotes are named for their **amniotic eggs**. The amnion is an extra membrane inside the egg that seals the embryo within a fluid environment. This innovation is what allowed the amniotes to exploit drier habitats than would support amphibians. Once on land, amniotes had no competition since the only other terrestrial animals were insects, and their small size suited them for a somewhat different lifestyle. The original amniotes quickly diversified and diverged into two lineages, **reptiles** and **mammals**.

REPTILES AND ARCHOSAURS

Modern reptiles are rather derived and structurally distant from the earliest reptiles of 300 million years ago. Most nevertheless share features that suggest how the original reptiles adapted to land so successfully. Reptile skin is thick and toughened with the protein **keratin**. An additional layer of keratin **scales** covers their skin, creating a very effective barrier to water loss. This means, however, that no oxygen can be absorbed through their skin, so reptilian lungs must be better-developed than amphibian lungs. In reptiles (and mammals) the lungs have complicated patterns of folds and bumps that create a huge surface for gas exchange. As a result their structure is more like a sponge than a balloon. The combination of dry skin, scales, efficient lungs, and amniotic eggs is so effective in dealing with dry environments that to this day reptiles are the most successful vertebrates in deserts.

The early reptiles diversified into groups as different as turtles, snakes, and lizards. One of the most successful reptile groups was the **archosaurs**: crocodiles and alligators, dinosaurs, and birds.

Archosaurs are more active than other reptiles, having higher metabolic rates and body temperatures. Reptiles are generally known as "cold-blooded" because they do not retain their body heat very well and become sluggish in cold temperatures. However archosaurs can generate enough heat to allow for prolonged activity. Indeed, crocodilians often have to cool themselves down by resting with their mouths gaping open so that their saliva will evaporate like sweat. Crocodiles use their extra energy for quick predatory movements and this is reflected in their limb structure. While most reptiles have a squat posture with their legs sprawling out at the sides, crocodilian legs are positioned closer to their bodies so that their feet are under their center of gravity. This raises the body into a posture conducive to running. Dinosaur skeletons exhibit an even more erect posture, and their legs are arranged more like running mammals and birds than crawling lizards.

Birds are the most active of all. Their metabolic rates are especially high and maintain a warm body temperature no matter what the weather. This means they must burn a lot of sugar, which means that they must maintain a high level of oxygen in their blood. Birds accomplish this in part with **double hearts** that completely partition oxygenated blood from the lungs away from the used, oxygen-depleted blood returning from the muscles. Bird hearts are often described as "four-chambered" to differentiate them from the hearts of amphibians and lizards which allow for some mixing of oxygenated and oxygen-depleted blood. These more primitive hearts are referred to as "three-chambered hearts," but such counting of chambers obscures many complex details of comparative anatomy.

The body scales of birds are expanded into **feathers**, which are one of the best insulators known (birds still have reptilian scales on their feet and occasionally on their faces). This allows them to retain their body heat and control their own body temperature and activity level. The combination of feathers and strong, active muscles allowed birds to develop flight, a way of life that has had a major influence in molding the skeleton and form of modern birds.

Archosaurs exhibit complex patterns of behavior, especially in rearing their young. When turtles or lizards lay their eggs, they abandon them and the hatchlings must fend for themselves. In contrast, crocodiles and alligators build nests and guard their young in a manner similar to birds. Fossilized dinosaur nests indicate that at least some species of dinosaurs did the same.

MAMMALS

It took some time for the archosaurs to appear. The first reptiles were actually dominated by another kind of amniote, the synapsids, or proto-mammals. Most of these animals died out in a mass extinction, opening up the environment to the early dinosaurs. The surviving synapsids evolved into the first mammals, but ironically they had a hard time competing with the dinosaurs and other archosaurs. It was not until the dinosaurs died out about 65 million years ago that mammals were able to diversify into their modern forms.

In many ways mammal evolution parallels that of birds. For example, mammals have double hearts analogous to those of birds. Mammals have neither scales nor feathers, but are covered in **hair**, which is made of keratin and develops from the same embryological skin structures that scales and feathers develop from. Hair is an insulator like feathers, but is not as effective (which is why coats are stuffed with down instead of hair). Nevertheless, mammals can occasionally overheat and mammalian skin is studded with **sweat glands** which can cool the skin when necessary.

Sweat glands were actually a major event in mammalian evolution, because they are the basis for **mammary glands**. The fluid these glands produce, **milk**, is fortified with protein and sugar so that it is a nutritious food for babies, but the glands work in much the same way as regular sweat glands do. In the most primitive mammals, the monotremes, milk oozes from a large patch of the mother's skin just like sweat, and her babies lap it up from her fur. In most mammals though the milk is delivered through specialized **nipples**. All such mammals have **lips** and muscular faces so that they can nurse (birds and reptiles do not have lips and their faces are mostly skin and bone). In many mammals these traits have been further modified to allow for complex forms of communication, both by facial expression and vocalization.

TETRAPOD LIMBS

All terrestrial vertebrates are **tetrapods**, meaning that they have four limbs. Some groups have lost a pair of limbs (e.g., whales) or all four (e.g., snakes) but in many cases the skeleton retains small vestigial bones where one would expect to find the missing limbs. In no species are there more than four limbs (which is why legends of flying horses or lions cannot be true). It seems clear that the ancestor of terrestrial vertebrates (probably a lobe-finned fish) had four limbs.

The bones in a tetrapod limb follow a definite pattern: a single bone extends from the body to the first joint (elbow or knee), a pair of bones extends to the next joint (wrist or ankle), and the limb ends in five fingers or toes. Sometimes groups of bones will be fused and appear to be one large bone. This is the case with the finger bones in bird wings and horse legs. Close examination of such structures often reveals suture lines where the different bones fused during the animal's development. The relative proportions of the bones may also vary from species to species: Reptiles and many mammals walk flat-footed, but running mammals and birds stand on their toes. As a result their leg bones are relatively short and their toe bones are relatively long.

Figure 14.4. Vertebrate forelimbs

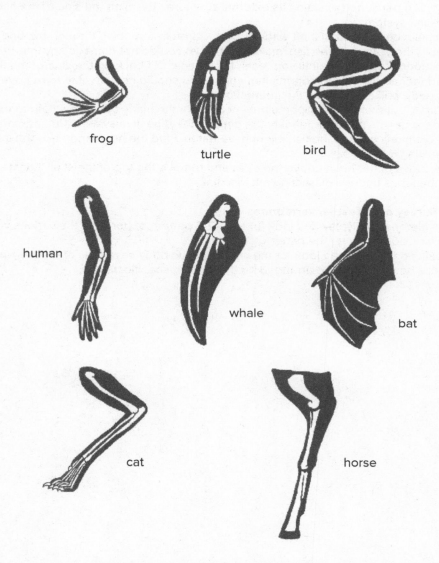

INVESTIGATIONS WITH DEUTEROSTOME ANIMALS

Investigation #1   Echinoderm embryology and diversity
1. **Sea star embryology:** Examine a prepared slide of sea star development. Identify the blastula and gastrula embryonic stages.
2. **Echinoderm diversity:**   Survey the different echinoderms on display. They are stiff because of their endoskeletons. Look for signs of the five-fold symmetry.

Investigation #2   Invertebrate chordates
1.   Examine one of the preserved specimens of the lancelet *Amphioxus* under a dissecting microscope and compare it to figure 14.2. Do you see evidence of segmentation?
2.   Study the dorsal side of the animal. Can you locate the nerve cord and notochord?

Investigation #3   Perch dissection
1.   Obtain a preserved perch and examine its external structure. Examine the side of the fish and try to find the lateral line system.
2.   Pull one operculum back and trim it off with scissors. Carefully cut down through the body wall from the operculum to the bottom of the fish, making sure that you do not damage any internal organs. Cut across the bottom of the fish until you reach the cloaca. Cut back up the side of the fish, past the lateral line, and then forward to the operculum again. You should now be able to remove a large section of the body wall and expose the internal organs.
3.   Examine the "leafy" gills where the operculum once was – the many thin layers help to expose as much blood to oxygen as possible. Identify the parts of the digestive system. Cut into the stomach and look for indications of what the fish might have eaten. Find the heart and trace the large vessels entering and exiting it.
4.   Cut around the sides of the head above the eyes and remove the top of the skull. Locate the brain and examine the lobes under a dissecting microscope.

Investigation #4   Survey of terrestrial vertebrates
1.   Examine the skeletons on display and look for the 1-2-5 pattern of bones in the various vertebrate limbs. Note how fusion can alter the pattern.
2.   Observe the skins on display and look for the characteristic body coverings of reptiles, mammals, and birds. Notice how feathers are arranged on the birds in specific tracts.

Important Terms

amniote
amniotic egg
amphibian
archosaur
bird
brain
cephalochordate
chordate
cloaca
double circulation
double heart
echinoderm
feather
gill arch
hair
heart
intestine
jaw
keratin
lateral line system
lip
liver
lung
mammal
mammary gland
milk
neural groove
neural tube
nipples
notochord
operculum
pharyngeal slits
post-anal tail
reptile
scale
stomach
sweat gland
swim bladder
tetrapod
vertebral column
vertebrate

CHAPTER 15
THE AGE STRUCTURE
OF A POPULATION

INTRODUCTION

We have seen that evolution depends on the relative rates of survival, mortality, and reproduction of the individual members of a population. These same factors determine the size and rate of growth of a population, and are thus central to the study of ecology as well as evolution. Since mortality and reproductive rates vary depending on the age of an individual, ecological study often requires a determination of the **age structure** of a population. Age structure is a description of the relative numbers of individuals of each age present in the population. By looking at the age structure in different ways, one can determine if a population is young and growing or old and dying out. It is also possible to use age structure data to calculate average life expectancies.

LIFE TABLES

There are two basic ways to study age structure. The **horizontal** approach collects data on all of the ages present in a population at some particular moment. It therefore generates a cross-section of the population with respect to time. For example, a horizontal study of the ages of oak trees in a woodlot might give the following data:

Age range, in years	Number of individuals
1-25	8
25-50	26
50-75	32
75-100	17
100-125	9
125-150	6
150-175	4

Such data are often represented graphically as **population pyramids**. Figure 15.1 shows a population pyramid for the hypothetical woodlot example. These graphs are called "pyramids" because they often show a large base of young individuals that shrinks with age because of mortality. The bulge in the middle of this graph suggests that the oaks in this woodlot are not producing as many new trees as they did in times past, a common problem in ecologically disturbed woodlands.

Figure 15.1. Population pyramid for a hypothetical population of oaks

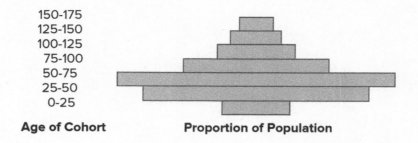

Age of Cohort   **Proportion of Population**

Horizontal studies are relatively simple to perform, as they require only a onetime sample of the population. They are good at detecting disturbances in the normal mortality and reproductive rates (for example, the "baby boom" in the United States after World War II appears as a large number of people in the 50-65 year old age group in current studies of the population). One problem with the horizontal approach is that it requires some method of determining the age of the various individuals in the sample population. In many plants and animals age can be estimated using morphological data such as size, number of growth rings, etc., but the accuracy of such estimates can vary. Horizontal studies also cannot be used for constructing life tables (below) unless one assumes that age structure, birth rate, and death rate are all constant.

The second approach to studying age structure is the **vertical** approach. A vertical study follows the lives of a **cohort** (group) of individuals born at the same time, with data being collected each year to see how many individuals survive to any given age. Thus if one finds that 50% of a population of octopuses die by age three, one can conclude that generally 50% of any similar population of octopuses would be less than 3 years old. Notice that in a vertical study each successive age group <u>must</u> be smaller than the preceding age group (since it is made up of survivors from the preceding groups) so that changes in age structure (such as the declining reproductive rate in our oak example or the "baby boom" in the modern U.S. population) could not be detected without comparing several cohorts. A major drawback to vertical studies is that they do not end until the last member of the cohort dies, and this can take several years for many species. Exceptionally long-lived organisms such as woody plants cannot be studied by this method at all (there are bristle-cone pine trees alive today which are older than all of recorded human history). However, the data from a vertical study is quite amenable to detailed statistical analysis in the form of **life tables**.

Life tables are used to estimate age-specific mortality, survivorship, and life expectancy. For an example of how to construct a life table, assume that a wildlife biologist is studying a pack of wolves. One summer he notices 9 new pups in the pack. He returns 2 years later and sees that only 6 of these pups are left. He puts radio collars on these six so that he can track them when they leave the pack and monitors them every two years until they all die. The data are shown below.

AGE	COHORT x	NUMBER IN COHORT Lx	NUMBER LIVING AT START lx	NUMBER DYING DURING X dx	PROB. OF DYING DURING X qx	PROB. OF SURVIVING INTERVAL X sx	ORGANISM YEARS LEFT TO LIVE Tx	LIFE EXPECTANCY ex
0-1	0	9	12	6	0.50	0.50	51	4.25 yrs.
1-3	1	6	6	0	0.00	1.00	42	7.00 yrs.
3-5	2	5	6	2	0.33	0.67	30	5.00 yrs.
5-7	3	4	4	0	0.00	1.00	20	5.00 yrs.
7-9	4	3	4	2	0.50	0.50	12	3.00 yrs.
9-11	5	2	2	0	0.00	1.00	6	3.00 yrs.
11-13	6	1	2	2	1.00	0.00	2	1.00 yrs.
13-15	7	0	0					

Only two columns of this life table are based on the field data: age (determined by how often observations could be made) and Lx, which shows the number of animals observed on each occasion. The other values are calculated. The method for calculating each value is given below.

Lx **(number in cohort)** This value is not calculated, it is empirical. Lx represents all of the individuals of an age group sampled at one time. This means that several ages are grouped together (age is a continuously variable trait – cf. chapter 2). We assume that the <u>average</u> age of a cohort is the middle of the range. Therefore there are 9 wolves of age 0.5 in cohort $L1$. We know from the next row in the table that there are only 6 individuals at an average age of 2, so quite a few must die during the first year. Since some must die before they reach the age of 0.5, there must originally have been more than 9 individuals at the beginning of this interval, and at the end of the interval there were less than 9. Estimating just how many were alive at the beginning and end of each interval, and how many died in between, is what the next three columns are for.

lx **(number at start)**   As indicated above, the number at the start of each interval must be estimated. The easiest way to do this is to start at the bottom (cohort #7) and work backwards. To do this we must first express lx in terms of Lx.

If Lx is the number of individuals at the midpoint of interval x, then it is the average of the number of individuals at the beginning of the interval and the end of the interval (which equals the beginning of the next interval):

$$Lx = (lx + lx+1)/2$$

This is algebraically equivalent to

$$lx = 2Lx - lx+1$$

Now in cohort #7 Lx equals 0. That means that everyone in the group is dead by this age, so the number of individuals at the beginning of the next interval, $lx+1$ ($l8$), will also equal 0. Therefore,

$$l7 = 2L7 - l8 = 2(0) - 0 = 0$$

We can now work backwards and calculate all values of lx:

$$l7 = 0$$
$$l6 = 2L6 - l7 = 2(1) - 0 = 2$$
$$l5 = 2L5 - l6 = 2(2) - 2 = 4 - 2 = 2$$
$$l4 = 2L4 - l5 = 2(3) - 2 = 6 - 2 = 4$$
$$l3 = 2L3 - l4 = 2(4) - 4 = 8 - 4 = 4$$
$$l2 = 2L2 - l3 = 2(5) - 4 = 10 - 4 = 6$$
$$l1 = 2L1 - l2 = 2(6) - 6 = 12 - 6 = 6$$
$$l0 = 2L0 - l1 = 2(9) - 6 = 18 - 6 = 12$$

$l0$ is the number alive at the very beginning, or the total size of the population before anyone dies. In this example, the statistics suggest that there were originally 12 pups born in the litter, but 3 of them died before the biologist saw any of them. There is no direct proof that this is so, but it is a hypothesis consistent with the observed mortality rates.

dx **(number dying during interval)**   The number of individuals which die during interval x is found by subtracting the survivors (that is, those alive at the beginning of the next interval) from those alive at the beginning of interval x:

$$dx = lx - lx+1$$

Eventually all of the individuals die, so the sum of all of the dx values should equal $l0$ (in this case, 12).

qx **(probability of dying during *x*)**   The chance of dying is the same as the proportion of those alive at the beginning of the time interval who die during the interval:

$$qx = dx/lx$$

This is the same thing as the **age specific mortality rate.** In our example, 6 of the original 12 individuals die the first year, for a mortality rate of 6/12 or 0.50. Stated another way, individuals in this population have a 50% chance of dying in their first year.

sx **(probability of surviving interval *x*)**   This is simply the converse of the previous statistic, found by subtracting it from 1. (Since you must either die or survive, the chance of one or the other happening must be 100%.) In this example, there is a 50% chance of surviving the first year, but for those who do, there is a 100% chance of living through the next 2 years — the weak pups die early but the survivors are cared for by the pack.

Tx **(organism years left to live)**   This is a kind of strange statistic which is calculated only in preparation for the final statistic, the life expectancy. It represents all of the years left to be lived by all of the remaining organisms in the sample, and is found by multiplying the number of individuals in a cohort by the time in each interval and then adding them together:

$$Tx = \sum Lx \text{ (interval)}$$

In our example, the first interval is 1 year but the remaining intervals are 2 years. Start from the bottom again: in cohort #6 there is only one individual who is going to live two more years, so *T6* equals 2. In cohort #5 there are 2 individuals who will each live two more years; one will die but one will survive to be cohort #6 and live a final year. Thus *T5* equals 4+2 or 6.

$$
\begin{aligned}
T6 &= 2L6 & = 2(1) & = & 2 \\
T5 &= 2L5 + T6 = 2(2) + & 2 = & 4 & +2 = 6 \\
T4 &= 2L4 + T5 = 2(3) + & 6 = & 6 & +6 = 12 \\
T3 &= 2L3 + T4 = 2(4) + & 12 = & 8 & +12 = 20 \\
T2 &= 2L2 + T3 = 2(5) + & 20 = & 10 & +20 = 30 \\
T1 &= 2L1 + T2 = 2(6) + & 30 = & 12 & +30 = 42 \\
T0 &= L0 + T1 = & & 9 & +42 = 51
\end{aligned}
$$

(*L0* is <u>not</u> multiplied by 2 - its interval is 1)

ex **(age-specific life expectancy)**   The **life expectancy** is found by dividing the organism-years by the number of individuals at the beginning of the interval:

$$ex = Tx/lx$$

In our example, any wolf born into this pack can expect, <u>on the average</u>, to live 4.25 years. Those which make it through the first year can expect to live another 7.00 years, and so on. The fact that life expectancy goes <u>up</u> after the first year indicates a significant **infant mortality rate**. After that, the life expectancy goes down with each interval as the animals have fewer and fewer years to live. Age-specific life expectancy is the same statistic which life insurance companies use to decide if someone is going to live long enough to be eligible for insurance.

SURVIVORSHIP CURVES

Life tables also supply data for **survivorship curves**. A survivorship curve illustrates how many members of a population are still alive at any particular age – that is, it is a graphic representation of how the population shrinks as it ages. Survivorship curves are typically plotted on a semi-log scale. The horizontal axis is linear and represents the age of the sample. The vertical axis is the logarithmic scale and is used to show the number of individuals at the beginning of each age interval (i.e., lx). As a result only large changes in the sample are visible on those portions of the graph where the population is large, but as the population shrinks, more details come out. Thus the scale automatically adjusts the plot so that the changes in population are seen in proportion to the size of the population at the time of the change.

The overall shape of a survivorship curve can give important information about a population. For example, a relatively straight diagonal line indicates a population with a steady death rate at all ages – the odds of dying are similar at any age. The sample life table used earlier in this lab gives such a curve. A curve that plummets quickly but then levels out illustrates a population with a high mortality rate for its young. The few individuals of such a population who manage to survive past a certain age tend to live very long, however. For example, a maple tree may produce thousands of seeds, but few will land on fertile ground. Of those that germinate, many will die while still small weak saplings. However, those few trees that make it past age 10 or 15 will probably survive for many decades or even centuries.

Humans illustrate a third type of curve: one that changes little at first but plummets at the end. This is because we tend to take good care of our young and try to ensure that every person who is born has the best chance possible of surviving. Before the advent of modern sanitation and health care, our survivorship curve was more diagonal – people had a strong chance of dying at almost any age. In industrial countries today the curves are much flatter as most people survive into old age. After about age 60 or 70, however, most human survivorship curves drop precipitously. Many biologists have argued that this indicates that there is a genetically determined maximum to the human life span that medical science can do little to extend.

Figure 15.1.   Types of survivorship curves

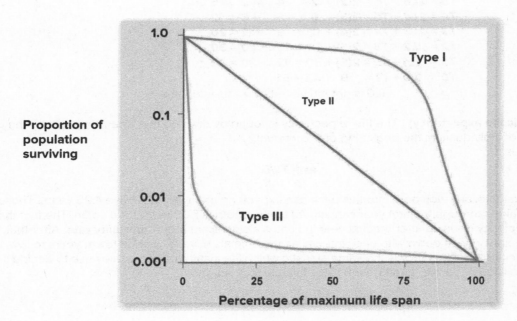

INVESTIGATING AGE STRUCTURE

Constructing a human life table

For this exercise the class will be taken to a cemetery to collect data for studying the age structure of a human population. The grave markers are an effective record of what age people were when they died and can be used as data for a vertical study. This is a little different from a classic vertical study since you are not following a well-defined cohort through life, but the data obtained are similar and will work just as well.

1. Each student will examine 10 gravestones and obtain the following data about the people buried beneath:

    a. sex   b. age of death   c. year died

    If you cannot determine the sex of the individual from the information on the marker, skip that grave and go to another.

2. Back in the laboratory, calculate the age of death for each individual in your sample. Divide your sample into four groups: men dying before and after 1935, and women dying before and after 1935. Then divide up the members of each group by age at death.

3. Because humans can live quite long, we will use different intervals than we did in the example. Our first interval will be one year but every other one will be 5 years –that is, interval one will be 0-1, two will be 1-6, then 6-11, 11-16, 16-21, etc. If the age at death falls exactly on the number between two intervals count that person as belonging to the smaller interval (e.g., a 1-year-old belongs in the 0-1 interval, a 6-year-old belongs in the 1-6 interval) unless the dates allow you to determine the age more precisely (e.g., 11 months belongs in 0-1 but 13 months belongs in 1-6). The last interval should have

    $lx = 0$ – no one survives to that age.

4. Your lab instructor will compile the data for the whole class. We will then tally the data from all of the lab sections to make a larger sample. This information will be given out at a later lab meeting and will be the basis for the life tables you construct.

5. Use the data to construct four separate life tables: men dying before 1935, men dying after 1935, women dying before 1935, and women dying after 1935.

    Note: The data you collect will be the number <u>dying</u> at each age, so it will be used for the dx column, not the Lx column. You will have to adjust your calculations accordingly: You will construct the lx column by adding up the data from the bottom of the dx column to the top, and construct the Lx column by averaging adjacent values in the lx column.

6. Once you have finished the life tables, consult the appropriate table to estimate how many more years <u>you</u> have left to live.

7. Plot the data from the lx columns of the tables as survivorship curves. Use different colored pencils or inks to draw all four survivorship curves on a single graph.

8. Examine your graph. Is the idea that the human life span is limited consistent with your data? If so, what age appears to be the limit? Is there much of a difference between males and females? Do you see evidence for high infant mortality in any of the samples?

Important Terms

age specific mortality rate
age structure
cohort
horizontal study
infant mortality rate
life expectancy
life table
population pyramid
survivorship curve
vertical study

The method of calculating life tables is adapted from Field and Laboratory Methods in General Ecology, 3rd edition, by Brower, Zar, and von Ende (1990).

CHAPTER 16
MICROBIAL COMMUNITIES

INTRODUCTION

Any ecological community consists of many species representing many different kinds of life. The terrestrial environments with which we are most familiar are dominated (in our minds at least) by only three phyla — vertebrates, arthropods, and angiosperms — yet these same environments depend on myriad unseen organisms to play vital ecological roles. Indeed, while it is quite possible to have a fully functioning ecosystem based solely on microorganisms, it is impossible to have a healthy ecosystem without microorganisms.

As with populations of other organisms, populations of microorganisms can be studied quantitatively and the interactions between different populations elucidated. Microbiological techniques can be used to sample water and soil specimens and culture the microbes present for identification. By comparing the numbers of colonies formed with the dilutions used to start the cultures, it is even possible to "count" the number of organisms present in the original sample. A typical gram of garden soil, for example, contains millions of bacteria and tens of thousands of algae and fungi.

Many of these organisms are important components of **biogeochemical cycles** (e.g., carbon cycle, nitrogen cycle) by which elements are recycled into forms usable by other creatures. Most are also prey for protozoans, slime molds, and the smaller roundworms and arthropods, and are thus at the very bottom of the community's food web.

THE WINOGRADSKY COLUMN: A CLOSED ECOSYSTEM

The **Winogradsky column** is a an artificially constructed community of microorganisms which is often used to illustrate the relationships between various soil organisms. It consists of a glass cylinder packed with mud enriched with added organic matter (such as shredded paper and old leaves) and certain minerals ($CaCO_3$, $CaSO_4$ and KH_2PO_4). The mud is wet with a mixture of pond water and several culture broths containing different types of bacteria.

The mud, pond water, and pure cultures all serve as sources for various bacteria and protists, creating a rich biota. These soon find areas in the column where they can thrive, dividing the column into different biotic zones. All that is needed to keep the system functioning is a suitable light source for the photosynthetic producers.

In the anaerobic environment deep within the column many types of bacteria, particularly the **pseudomonads**, are able to break down the polysaccharides present (primarily cellulose and pectin from the paper and leaves) and use this material for fermentation. This produces many waste products such as lactic acid, butyric acid, ethanol, and other organic compounds. These wastes can be further oxidized by other bacteria in processes that simultaneously reduce nitrate and nitrite ions to ammonia and nitrogen (this is an important part of the **nitrogen cycle**).

Because Winogradsky columns are enriched with calcium sulfate, they also have a sulfur cycle. Some bacteria reduce sulfate ions to H_2S, causing a smell like rotten eggs. The reaction of hydrogen sulfide with iron to form FeS makes mud black. The hydrogen sulfide is used by **purple** and **green sulfur bacteria** in place of water in their mode of photosynthesis, so these organisms can be found growing in colored patches against the glass in areas of H_2S production. These patches of black (sulfide-producing), purple, and green bacteria are a striking aspect of the Winogradsky column.

Near the top of the mud, where oxygen and nitrogen are available, nitrogen-fixing cyanobacteria may be found. Above them, in the aqueous portion of the environment, are the algae and protozoans. The protozoans will consume different bacteria as food, but are relatively sensitive to the buildup of bacterial wastes such as H_2S and acid fermentation products. Various fungi can live here as well.

INVESTIGATIONS WITH A WINOGRADSKY COLUMN

Each group will be given a Winogradsky column to study. There are many possible ways to sample a Winogradsky column. The protists in the top water can be observed microscopically and identified and counted. The bacteria and fungi could be sampled and grown on media plates, but the diversity makes this impractical – many separate media would be needed for the different nutritional needs of the different organisms, and each type of medium would have to be used for several dilutions at each depth sampled. Hundreds of plates would be required per column. However, the colored colonies of the sulfur cycle can be seen without further culturing, and these are among the more interesting creatures living in the column. You can "count" them simply by measuring the size of their colonies.

Investigation #1   Survey of protists in the water phase
The original water used at the top of the column contained many algae and protozoa as well as some tiny animals – roundworms, annelids, and arthropods. The column has aged several weeks since then and not all of these groups have survived.
1.   Each member of the group should make a wet mount slide from the liquid above the mud and look for protists. Try to identify any you find at least by phylum.
2.   Now expand your observations. Fast-moving creatures can be slowed down with a drop of 1% methyl cellulose. If you have trouble seeing the non-pigmented cells, stain the slide with methylene blue. Are there any animals in the water?

Investigation #2   Quantitative profile of sulfur bacteria
When a Winogradsky column is made, a quantity of calcium sulfate and calcium carbonate (about a tablespoon, or 15 ml, of each) is placed in the bottom and the mud layered on top. The sulfate and carbonate diffuse through the mud as the column ages. Since carbonate is a base, a pH gradient forms, so that the bottom of the column is about pH 8 and the top is closer to 7. This can affect the distribution of bacteria from top to bottom.
1.   Examine the side of the column. Look for black, purple, and green colonies (the background mud is gray). These are each part of the sulfur cycle. They are all obligate anaerobes, so they should all be at least a centimeter or two below the top of the mud. You may also see some red or rust-colored colonies near the top of the mud. They are not sulfur-metabolizing species, but can be counted as non-sulfur photosynthetic bacteria.
2.   There should be a centimeter scale taped to the side of the column (if there is not, make one). You will use this to determine the depth of each colony. Starting 1 cm from the very bottom, measure the width around the column of each colored colony (use a flexible plastic ruler). If the colony is in several small patches at a given depth, total the length of each at that depth. For example, if at 1 cm from the bottom there are three 1 cm wide colonies and a single big colony 3.4 cm wide, the width at that depth should be recorded as 6.4 cm. Do not measure the height of the colonies – if they are tall they will be measured at other depths and if they are short they will only be measured once.
3.   Repeat the process for each type of colony every 2 cm until you reach the top of the mud. Tabulate your results showing the width of each color colony from bottom to top.

4. On one page of your notebook, draw several histograms, one for each color colony (there should be at least 3 – black, purple, and green – but may be more if other colors are present). The horizontal axis should show distance from the bottom and the vertical should indicate the width of the colony at that depth. Thus each histogram should be a profile of the amount of bacteria by depth. Line the histograms up over each other when you draw them so that you can compare them easily.
5. Is one type of bacteria more common at the bottom and another at the top? Are any other patterns apparent?

Important Terms

biogeochemical cycle
green sulfur bacteria
nitrogen cycle
pseudomonad
purple sulfur bacteria
Winogradsky column

APPENDIX A
MAINTAINING A LABORATORY NOTEBOOK

You will need to maintain a record of your laboratory work in a bound notebook of graph-ruled paper. Although different scientists may have different styles of maintaining notebooks, the format prescribed below would be acceptable in most research laboratories.

The point of keeping a notebook is that you will have an accurate record of events as they occur. It is therefore important that you **make your notes directly in your notebook during lab – do NOT take them on scrap paper to be recopied later**. While recopying produces a neater notebook, it usually produces a less complete notebook, as the scrap paper notes are frequently lost.

Format
1. The notebook is a <u>permanent</u> record. All entries must be in non-water soluble ink. Mistakes should be scratched out with one or two horizontal lines. Although the notebook needs to be legible, accuracy is more important than neatness.
2. Records are to be kept on one side of the paper only - the right (front). The back of the page (left side) may be used as scratch paper for calculations. Scratch calculations may be written in pencil. Records kept on the wrong side of the paper will not be graded and can be informal and messy.
3. The first two pages should be left blank at first so a **Table of Contents** can be created as the book is filled in. The Table of Contents should list each experiment in order, by title, with the first page it appears on. The Table of Contents should be updated continuously.
4. At the top of every page should be written the **title** of the experiment recorded on that page, the **date** the notes were recorded, and the **page number** (if the notebook does not have pre-printed page numbers).
5. Each new experiment should begin on a fresh page, even if the previous page is not completely filled.

Records should be as complete as possible. Students seldom record too much information; they often record too little. Every notebook should make clear exactly what experiments were performed, how they were conducted, and what results were observed. Items which must be recorded include:

Materials   The name of any living or prepared specimens (genus and species, if possible), the composition of solutions, and the source of species-specific materials such as enzymes should all be listed. It is not necessary to list common ordinary items such as glassware – this section is simply a reference for those special materials you would need to obtain if you were to repeat the experiment.

Procedures   A brief <u>summary</u> of the procedure published in the lab manual is usually sufficient - it is unnecessary to recopy the procedure verbatim. However, any changes made to the published procedure, whether dictated by the lab instructor or by special circumstances, must be noted. It is convenient to have this section done before you come to lab.

Raw data   This section should list any measurements, instrument readings, and qualitative observations. Tables are often appropriate for data. Certain pieces of physical data, such as chromatograms and instrument printouts, should be attached to the notebook. (If a lab partner has such data in another notebook, then this should be noted here.) Sketches and diagrams also belong in this section. It is permissible to make sketches in pencil, but ink is encouraged for permanence and clarity. For purely descriptive labs, this section will essentially be the entire record. <u>Again, all data should be recorded in the notebook as it is observed</u> – not recopied from scratch paper later.

Formulas & calculations   Calculated values and the formulas used to derive them should be recorded next. The actual calculations can be written on the scratch pages or done on a calculator – the formal record consists of a table of the final calculated values and the data used in the calculations. For example, if an experiment involved the densities of several objects, a table could be made giving the mass, volume, and density of each. The mass and volume would be data, as they are actual measurements, but the density would have to be calculated from these data. Such a table would serve as a record of both data and calculations. Complex calculations may require multiple tables. In the example above, if the volumes of the objects were not measured directly but calculated from measurements of height, length, and width, then these measurements might constitute a second table.

Graphs   All graphs of data should be drawn in the notebook. An experiment may generate many graphs. Some experiments call for graphs to be made on semi-log paper. This can be attached to the notebook as needed.

Conclusions   A summary of the experiment is useful. This section should contain a statement of what was or was not demonstrated by the experiment. Any speculations supported by the data may be included here. Problems encountered during the experiment should be discussed in the conclusion along with suggestions for further experiments that might resolve these problems. In order to write a good conclusion you will have to spend some time after lab reflecting on what happened. It is here you will appreciate having taken good notes so that you can answer any new questions that arise.

APPENDIX B
USING SCIENCE RESOURCES IN THE LIBRARY

INTRODUCTION

Biologists generally try to do experiments or field observations on topics that interest them personally. Luckily, many of these topics are interesting or useful to others as well, so there is a demand for people to write about their research in books and scientific journals. Over the years libraries have become filled with a vast amount of scientific information. Researchers are expected to use this information and become familiar with what others have done in their field – that way they can discuss and write about their own work in a broad context while not wasting time on questions that others have already answered. Therefore an important skill biologists must master is how to access this existing information efficiently.

As you probably know, books in a library are arranged according to subject and are indexed in a computer catalog so that they can be easily located. Journals are more complex because they are constantly growing. This means that they contain the most up-to-date information (which is critical for scientists), but it also means that their indexes must grow too. Indeed, several journals are now published that are nothing more than indexes to other journals. In this section we will review the process of locating books about biology and also learn how to find journal articles using several commonly used indexes.

BOOKS AND JOURNALS

Although we generally think of books first when we think of libraries, books are of limited usefulness to scientists. That is because science is an ongoing process, so books quickly become dated. Nevertheless, they can be useful references for information that does not change much. In biology, one common use for books is for reading about basic taxonomy. For example, if you are assigned a research paper that must focus on a particular family or class of organisms, a general book on those organisms could give you examples of various taxa and explain their basic characteristics. This would then make it much easier to find and read up-to-date journal articles on the subject.

Research journals are essentially magazines published by professional groups of scientists. They are not directed at the general public and are highly technical. Do not confuse popular scientific magazines with research journals – popular magazines like *Discover* and *Scientific American* have articles about science, but they are not technical papers written by scientific researchers. A true research article will have a bibliography, notes in the text that cite the bibliography, and usually will begin with a summary (called an **abstract**). It will focus on brand new research performed by the authors. A few professional journals, such as *Nature* and *Science*, contain both research papers and less formal news articles. The research articles in these journals are excellent, but the news articles are more like what you would encounter in a popular magazine. Generally, in such a journal the true research articles are towards the back.

There are books in the library that are in-between books and journals. These are bound, hard cover books, but they contain long articles that look like research papers. Such books are often published yearly so they are more up-to-date than regular books. These books contain **review articles** written by prominent scientists. A review article is very useful because it cites and summarizes research articles on a particular topic from the past few years. If you are lucky enough to find a recent review article on your topic you will have a tremendous head start on your research, because the review article will contain a huge bibliography of research papers and tell you what is in them. It will also give you the names of scientists who work in the field so you can look up other articles by them. A review article does not count as a research article because it is summarizing other papers rather than reporting new research, but it can still be very useful. The titles of many books of review articles begin with "*Annual Review of —-*."

FINDING LIBRARY BOOKS

Most libraries are organized according to the Library of Congress system. In this system each book is given a **call number** beginning with one or two letters. The first letter signifies what broad subject area the book falls under. For example, the call numbers for all science books begin with the letter "Q." The second letter denotes a subcategory of the subject and the numbers after the letters tell exactly where in the classification scheme the book belongs. Books are located on the shelves by subject letter in alphabetical order and then in numerical order within each subject area.

The Library of Congress system was devised at the turn of the century <u>after</u> the Library of Congress had already accumulated a huge number of books it did not know how to organize. The system was designed to handle large numbers of books efficiently, but it was never very systematic – it was built around the books the Library owned at the time. For example, all science book call numbers start with "Q," but there is no subcategory for biology. Instead, QH is used for "natural history" (an old term meaning the study of nature), QK is for botany, QL for zoology, QM for human anatomy, QP for physiology, and QR for bacteriology. All biology books are squeezed into one of these categories. In practice this makes it difficult to predict where you might find a particular book, so you must use the **catalog**.

The catalog is an index of all of the books in a library. It was originally kept in a file of cards, but libraries have switched to computerized systems now. Online catalogs are sufficiently complex that many libraries subscribe to an external catalog provider, which often has the added benefit of providing access to the catalogs of several libraries at once. The catalog is searchable in three ways: by author, title, and subject. The subject listings are more specific than the call letter designations and allow for cross-referencing. For example, if you wanted a book about dogs, you would not want to search through all of the hundreds of books in the QL (zoology) section – instead you would do a search on "dogs" and find the exact call numbers of the listed books. You would find several books which may or may not be near each other on the shelves (some might be under QL, others under QH or even QP).

ON-LINE SEARCHES

The internet has created fast ways to find information. Much of the information on the internet itself is of very poor quality, but a few web sites offer search engines that will search published journals for articles. These electronic search engines are very convenient, but do have limits. One such limitation is that the URL addresses may change or the site may go out of business suddenly. Another is that many search engines have become subscription access only. Libraries will subscribe to some but not others.

A very useful search engine, *Pubmed*, can be found at:

<u>http://www.ncbi.nlm.nih.gov/</u>

This web page is run by the National Center for Biotechnology Information and the National Library of Medicine, and is sponsored by the National Institutes of Health and is open to the public. Because *Pubmed* is run by the Library of Medicine, it only searches professional research articles, so it is ideally focused for scientific searches. Unfortunately, it is too focused for many searches, because it only deals with medicine, human physiology, and gene sequences. You will find little about botany or evolution and ecology here. Nevertheless, it can be a convenient place to begin a literature search.

BIOSIS

One general search engine is called **Basic BIOSIS**. This system allows for easy to use keyword searches that generate lists of articles, most of which are linked to abstracts. Basic BIOSIS is designed to be simple, but it is often adequate for class assignments. **BIOSIS Previews** is a more advanced search engine with more features than Basic BIOSIS.

CITATION INDEX

When scientists write a journal article, they cite (refer to) earlier published articles on the same subject. That way they add to an existing body of knowledge in an orderly fashion. This means that once you have found an article on a topic you can use the bibliography of that article to find more articles on the topic. Of course, all of those cited articles are older than the one that lists them – they had to be already in print in order to be cited. So while the bibliography may lead you to other articles, you will be going back to older and older work as you track them down.

Oddly enough, there is an index that allows you to go from an article to *newer* articles in the field. The *Science Citation Index* tells you what new articles cite, and therefore build upon, older articles you may have from years ago. Say for example that you are a paleontologist specializing in the dinosaurs that lived during the Jurassic period 200 million years ago. Researching on how the continents moved during the Jurassic, you find a reference to a famous paper called "Sea-floor spreading and continental drift" that Xavier Le Pichon wrote back in 1968. While this paper may have been a breakthrough in its time, the field must have advanced since then. But anything in Le Pichon's bibliography would be even older. How do you find out what has been added to this topic since then? The *Science Citation Index* tells you who cites that paper every year. If you search on Le Pichon through the *Science Citation Index* you will get a list of newer articles that contain his paper in their bibliographies. The *Citation Index* can be especially helpful if you need to find out whether someone's observations have been confirmed over time or if a theory has survived experimental testing.

APPENDIX C
WRITING SCIENCE PAPERS

INTRODUCTION

Written assignments are a part of any college course and sooner or later you will be asked to prepare some kind of paper for your biology class. There are two basic types of written papers that are used in science – the lab report and the research, or topic, paper. The objectives of both assignments are to increase student's familiarity with concepts and procedures by writing about them and to practice modes of style used by professional scientists. Since scientific experiments do little to advance knowledge if their results are not communicated to other scientists (or the public in general), effective communication is essential to all scientists.

Papers should follow standard formats for legibility: they should be typed, double-spaced, and have one-inch margins. Papers should not incorporate unusual printer fonts. Automated spell-checking is very helpful, but should not be considered a substitute for careful proofreading.

LABORATORY REPORTS

A lab report is basically a summary of an experiment or related group of experiments. It should be as brief as completeness allows. While the lab report contains an accurate description of the experiment and its results, it does not include a complete step-by-step procedure or listing of raw data. The reader of the lab report should be able to understand what the experiment was expected to accomplish, how it was performed, and what it actually demonstrated.

By convention, scientific reports have historically been written in a formal style of passive voice: colloquialisms are avoided, as are first- and second-person pronouns. Students are encouraged to browse the technical literature available in the university library in order to familiarize themselves with this style. (The portion of Appendix C concerning laboratory reports is written in such a formal style; the rest of Appendix C, and, for that matter, the rest of this book, is written in a less formal style. The student may compare these sections as a way of exploring the different styles. Careful attention should be paid to the lack of pronouns, and the changes in language that result, in the formal style.) While not all courses (or even professional journals) require the use of formal passive voice, it is a useful skill to practice so that it may be correctly used when needed.

The basic sections of a laboratory report are:

Title   The title should be descriptive of the experiments or the phenomena studied. Titles should not simply refer to a laboratory exercise by number, nor should they be overly creative.

Introduction   This section presents the context and rationale of an experiment. Most experiments are designed to prove or disprove a particular hypothesis, or logical inference based on established data. Thus, experiments systematically extend the boundaries of knowledge. The experiments in this book are intended to demonstrate or illustrate well-known phenomena.

Materials and Methods   This section summarizes how the experiment was actually carried out. Materials may be described parenthetically in the description of the procedure (e.g., "Cockroaches (*Periplaneta* sp.) were killed by exposure to diethyl ether and preserved in formalin solution (10% formaldehyde) prior to dissection.") or listed separately before the methods. Whichever format is chosen should be used consistently throughout the report. If abbreviations are used, a list should be provided, but excessive or unusual abbreviations should be avoided.

Results   This is the presentation of the data. All observations and measurements pertinent to the conclusion are included, often with tables, graphs, or diagrams. This section is <u>strictly</u> <u>descriptive</u>, as all conclusions are to be presented in the discussion section. <u>The "results" section must include a narrative description of the data</u> — it should not consist solely of an array of tables and graphs without any text.

Discussion   The discussion section completes the report. This is where conclusions are drawn and general principles described. Conditions which affect the results are also described here, as are attempts to explain unexpected results. A well-written discussion should relate the results to the introduction.

TOPIC PAPERS

Topic papers are intended to be a review of technical research papers published about the assigned topic. The topic paper will cover more information than any single journal article that you find. A good model for the paper would be a <u>review article</u> published in a scientific journal. Unfortunately, citations to articles from **BIOSIS** or other search tools seldom tell you whether a particular article is a review article or not. Several series of books are published that contain collections of review articles, for example, ***Annual Review of Cell Biology***, ***Annual Review of Microbiology***, ***Annual Review of Biochemistry***, ***Annual Review of Ecology and Systematics***, ***Annual Review of Genetics***, ***Annual Review of Physiology***, etc. You might want to look at one of these books to see what the format is like. If you are lucky enough to find a recent review article on your topic you have it made, because the bibliography of a review article will list dozens of research articles on the topic. It will also tell you the names of many experts in the field so you can also use author and citation indexes to find even more articles.

Although a scientific topic paper is similar to research papers in other disciplines, the heavy emphasis on technical research poses special problems. Specific advice for writing science papers follows:

- All of your general information and uncited background explanations (e.g., based on what you read in your text or heard in lecture) should be limited to the introduction of your paper. This should be short — boil it down and move on to the research quickly!

- The body of the paper should summarize the contents of the cited papers and compare them. It is almost like a series of short book reports. However, you should also work to bring the information from the different papers together into a coherent discussion.

- Since this paper is intended to review published articles, every paragraph (except perhaps the introduction and conclusion) should have **at least** one citation. If you are not discussing someone's research, you are probably not saying anything important.

- Use the most recent references you can find — this is a report on **modern** ideas about the topic. Find as many sources as you can that were published in the last few years. You may find that the authors are arguing with each other; that's OK, present it that way. The more recent the research, the less sure people are about what it means.